GOOD OLD DOCTOR MAC

THOMAS A. McNAMARA
Family Physician
1856 – 1927

GOOD OLD DOCTOR MAC

THOMAS A. McNAMARA
Family Physician
1856 – 1927

Robert F. McNamara

Devon Press
Utica, New York

GOOD OLD DOCTOR MAC

Parts of *Good Old Doctor Mac* have been serialized under the title "Old-style
Family Physician: Corning's Doc Mac" in *The Crooked Lake Review*
(Hammondsport, New York), issues 34 – 37 (January – April, 1991).

ISBN 0-9701516-1-6

Library of Congress Cataloging-in-Publication Data

McNamara, Robert Francis, 1910-
  Good old doctor Mac : Thomas A. McNamara : family physician, 1856-1927 /
by Robert F. McNamara.
      p. ; cm.
  Includes bibliographical references and index.
  ISBN 0-9701516-1-6 (alk. paper)
  1. McNamara, Thomas A., 1856-1927. 2. Physicians (General
practice)--United States--Biography. 3. Family medicine--United
States--History.
  [DNLM: 1. McNamara, Robert Francis, 1910- 2. Family Practice--United
States--History. 3. Family Practice--history--United States. WZ 100 M4785g
2004] I. Title.
  R154.M288M38 2004
  610'.92--dc22

                    2004014607

DEVON PRESS
NORTH COUNTRY BOOKS, INC.
311 Turner Street
Utica, New York 13501

To the memory of

Thomas Leo McNamara, M.D.
"Young Doc Mac"

a chip off the old block
(1888 – 1981)

Table of Contents

Preface

This is the true story of an old-style physician who practiced many years ago in a small community in western New York. The career of my father, Thomas Alexander McNamara of Corning, New York, extended over a transitional period in American and medical history. He was no major figure in either national or medical annals; but he did typify the conscientious medic of the era, a man of professional integrity and civic pride.

My narrative is based on available documents and abundant reminiscences: my own, of course, as his last-born son; those of relatives and close friends; and particularly those of his former patients and their families. The latter group of witnesses have always been eager to relate the "Doc Mac" anecdotes that are a gracious part of their family lore.

When I wrote the first draft of this memoir in the 1980s, my prime motive was to furnish my nephews and nieces with at least a quick sketch of their very special grandparent. From the outset, however, I recognized that his story was attractive, and could appeal to many other readers who admire good men. Medic he was, of course, around the clock; but that very profession brought him into broad contact with so many of the grand themes of human experience: The struggle of immigrants, for instance, to "start all over again". Business enterprise: its ethics, its successes, its failures. Politics, noble and less noble. Religion and science. War and peace. Life and death. And, naturally, everyday family life in a small town, with its particular joys and sorrows. Doctor Mac faced the challenges that Corning offered, large and small, yet persevered in the respect of his fellow citizens.

One kinsman, who read my original "family" version of the biography did wonder whether I had painted a portrait "too good to be true". It was a valid question. I was only sixteen when he died. Am I able even now to judge him critically? I have long since waived that query. Those who knew him best spoke of him only in praise, and I accept their judgment.

Here, then, is the unadorned profile of an able "G.P." ("general practitioner") of medicine, and a devout and decent individual.

There have been many such physicians – men and women alike – in national and world history. Caring, but duly appreciated?

I offer this little book as a salute to them all.

Robert F. McNamara
Archivist
Archives, Diocese of Rochester in America

November 18, 2004
Feast day of Bd. Grimoaldo Santamaria, C.P.

Acknowledgments

Even a brief biography is the achievement of a host of authors. I shall therefore say explicit thanks only to a token number of my "co-authors," while assuring the unnamed that they, too, have my deep gratitude.

First of all, I am grateful to the following for reading and critiquing my manuscript: Sister Kathleen Milliken of the Rochester Sisters of Mercy; Richard J. Collins, M.D., of Avon, N.Y.; Emerson Klees, Editor/Publisher, Cameo Press, Rochester, N.Y.; Joseph C. O'Dea, D.V.M., of Geneseo, N.Y.; Edward C. Atwater. M.D., of Rochester, N.Y.; Wendell Tripp, Editor Emeritus, *New York History* of Cooperstown, N.Y.; Carole L. Mihalko, current associate editor, *New York History*; and Virginia Wright, Chairman of Publications, Corning-Painted Post Historical Society.

I am indebted to several individuals and institutions for graphics and photos and the permission to reproduce them.

The Tate Picture Library (Millbank, London, U.K.) has given leave to print on the cover, "The Doctor," the well-known Tate Gallery painting by the British artist Sir Luke Fildes (1843-1927).

For our "Picture Album" (inside the book), Twila O'Dell, Steuben County Historian, has kindly provided an 1873 map of the lower townships of Steuben County. Roger Grigsby, director of Benjamin Patterson Inn Museum in Corning, has supplied us with copies of two pictures from the archives of the Corning-Painted Post Historical Society: an 1873 photo of Corning's "Concert Block," and a bird's-eye engraving (1882) of Corning village. James G. Laragy, prominent Rochester, N.Y. photographer, has restored for our use two photographs: the inauguration of Corning's Denison Park (1909) and a contingent of departing World War I draftees posed with the officers of the local Exemption Board.

David Schoen, Director of Libraries, Niagara University (Niagara University P.O., N.Y.) has sent us an 1870s view of that institution's campus, permission to publish it having been accorded by Linus Ormsby, University Director of Public Relations. Lastly, Andrea Jackson, graduate assistant at the archives of New York University, has helpfully secured for us, with license to print it, an early engraving of the N.Y.U. "University Building" (Hinshelwood View, 1836).

Several members of the McNamara and Dwyer families deserve thanks for their unwavering interest in this publication: Elizabeth V. Bangs (Camp Hill, PA); John P. Sheeran (N. Clarendon, VT); Noel S. Drower (New City, N.Y.); Patricia S. DeMarco (Ho-Ho-Kus, N.J.); Katherine A. McNamara (Evanston, IL); Susan M. McNamara-Ten Eyck (Dayton, OH); D. David and Shirley K. Griffin (Hammondsport, N.Y.); Ann Maloney (Rochester, N.Y.).

The following individuals merit special notice: James L. McNally, Ph.D. (Geneseo, N.Y.); Sister M. Esther Carstater, R.S.M., Librarian, Our Lady of Mercy High School (Rochester, N.Y.); Martha and William Treichler, Editors, *The Crooked Lake Review* (Hammondsport, N.Y.); Jeanne Marie and Alfred J. Bello (Rochester, N.Y.); Daniel L. Killigrew, Jr., Mayor of Corning, 1984-1987; Thomas P. Dimitroff and Lois S. Janes, authors of *History of the Corning-Painted Post Area: 200 Years in Painted Post Country* (Corning, N.Y., 1976, 1991); Richard V. ("Dick") Peer, local history columnist ("Peering"), in the *Leader* (Corning, N.Y.); and William G. Canfield, Reference Librarian, Southeast Steuben County Library (Corning, N.Y.).

Finally, I must express my appreciation to Mrs. Ellen Brannin for preparing the typescript of *Good Old Doctor Mac*. She has brought to that task not only all the computer skills that the author lacks, but a wonderful enthusiasm.

— CHAPTER ONE —

From Ballycahane to Adrian

Strollers along Manhattan's lower Broadway in the chilly evening of March 7, 1882, were startled by an impromptu parade. Scores of soberly dressed young men suddenly came dancing up the gaslit street, wall-to-wall across the roadway.

Observers would have scarcely believed that this was the graduating class of the New York University Medical School. Only a few minutes before, all 213 of them had sat solemnly in the commencement auditorium, their many beards making them look quite serious and professional. (In those days a doctor's beard was a credential almost as important as his diploma.) They had earnestly taken the Hippocratic oath, traditional pledge of the physician, promising to preserve life and never destroy it; to respect their patients and never betray or corrupt them; and to uphold in their own lives the honor of the medical profession. Then they had mounted the platform to receive the huge sheep-skin scrolls of their doctorates, engraved in Latin phrases and signed with a flourish by Doctors Alfred G. Post, John C. Draper, Alfred L. Loomis, and the other beaming professors on the dais who sat applauding each recipient.

The carefree snake-dance that followed dismissal might have

1

seemed shocking, but only to those who were unaware that in the 1880's the medical course of studies was just two years long. Therefore, behind those grave medical beards were 200 young heads. The new doctors had the rest of their lives to be sober-sides. This evening they had a right to kick up their heels.

This story of the "dance" up Broadway comes from Dr. John Dorning, a member of the Class of 1882. He was to become a prominent physician in New York City. Most of his class were from the Gotham area or planned to practice there. But two of the group were "hicks" from Adrian, in Steuben County, one of the tiniest and most remote hamlets of upstate New York. The "hicks" were Dr. Daniel L. McNamara and his brother, younger by one year, Dr. Thomas A. McNamara. Thomas Alexander McNamara, my father, is the "Doctor Mac" of our story.

I used to visit Adrian every few years. It is about nine miles southeast of the city of Hornell, and about four miles southeast of the village of Canisteo. I always had to watch out carefully for Adrian. You could be out of it before you realized you were in it. Fifty, perhaps even forty years ago, the settlement had a self-respecting rural tidiness. Today it is very dilapidated.

I use "hicks" because smug natives of New York City would probably have fixed that term on anybody who lived north of the Bronx. But "hick" as "farmer" was incorrect. Dan and Tom McNamara were the sons of an immigrant railroader, Patrick McNamara.

Patrick was born in 1822 at Ballycahane, Manister, (Monaster) near Croom, County Limerick, Ireland. He emigrated to the U.S.A., probably in 1850, with his parents, Daniel and Ann McInerney McNamara, and several siblings. They located at Hornellsville, New York. In 1850, Hornellsville ("Hornell" only since 1905) was a wee hamlet, but on the point of becoming the western center of a brand-new state-wide railroad, the New York and Erie. The Erie Canal, finished in 1825, had successfully joined New York Harbor with Lake Erie by a waterway across the State's northern tier of counties; but the southern tier of counties profited little by Dewitt Clinton's "Big Ditch". The

New York and Erie Railroad was the counter-challenge of the "friends of the Southern Tier." New York State's first trunk line, it was laid west to Buffalo athwart the hilly, forested, southern counties.

As 1851 approached, Hornellsville doubled in population. Scores of newcomers arrived to build a depot, sheds, repair and maintenance shops, and residences. Rumors of job opportunities along the new right-of-way were surely in the air. Had they even reached Ballycahane? Had the Daniel McNamaras purchased a one-way family fare from County Limerick to Hornellsville?

Once arrived, Patrick McNamara got a job with the New York and Erie. He started as a section hand (or "gandy-dancer"). But being an able man with a brisk sense of leadership, he rose quickly to foreman of a section. The section assigned to him seems to have been from Hornell east to Cameron Mills.

When Daniel McNamara settled in this Erie boomtown he registered his family at St. Ann's, the mostly-Irish parish that served not only Hornellsville but much of the neighboring countryside. As early as June 14, 1854, Patrick McNamara and Frances McMullen were married in St. Ann's Church. Frances was the daughter of Alexander McMullen (1779-1867) and Mary Mooney McMullen, a Catholic couple from County Antrim in the largely Protestant province of Ulster. The McMullens lived in an Irish farming community at Greenwood, a dozen miles south of Hornellsville.

Adrian then boasted its own little railroad station. It was so handy to the site of Patrick's labors that he and Frances decided to make their home there. Pat himself had a little house built on a small lane that faced the Erie tracks. The floorplan was one much used in those days: on the left, a two-story section whose ridgepole ran at right angles to the street; and on the right, a one-story ell, set back somewhat to provide space for a porch. Forty years ago the little homestead was still quite presentable, and the "cartwheel" penny that Uncle Alexander McNamara, when a kid there, had nailed high up the west siding, was still in place, though covered with paint. At my last visit the little building was in such disrepair that only the presence of a barking dog in the back yard suggested it was lived in at all.

In this small house Pat and Fannie McNamara raised a sizable family, two girls and five boys. (A sixth boy, second-last among Fannie's children, died in infancy.) Daniel came first, born July 14, 1855. Thomas Alexander followed, on December 16, 1856. William was born on August 25, 1858; and Alexander on November 30, 1859. Then came the two girls: Mary (September 21, 1861) and Frances (May 10,1863). Last in line was Patrick Junior. The pastor of St. Ann's Church apparently forgot to register his baptism, but the year was 1865.

Around 1890, on the occasion of a family reunion with their widowed father, the Mac boys and girls posed with him for a family photograph. If I do say so, they were an impressive – even a handsome – family. Old Patrick sat in front, clean-shaven, unsmiling, and patriarchal, his shock of silver hair parted on the side. Seated beside him were Mary ("Peacock Mary," they called her; stylish, shrewd and saucy) and Frances Jr. (dignified and imperious). The five brothers stood behind this seated trio, modeling the three types of beards and mustaches that were most fashionable in 1890.

To judge by the healthy appearance of the Mac septet, Adrian had been a good place to raise a family. It was indeed healthful in the narrow but fertile valley of the little Canisteo River, which meandered east amid the wooded hills. Actually only one of the children, Will, had a congenital weakness: the asthma he inherited from his mother. Adrian also contributed to their social formation in that most of their immediate neighbors were neither Irish nor Catholic. Unlike so many Irish immigrant families, who chose to settle in big cities, these McNamaras grew up, not in a crowded Hibernian ghetto, but in a spacious Yankee countryside where they were unavoidably schooled in Yankee values.

Even in this quiet hamlet, however, Patrick and Frances had to keep a close watch over their brood lest they go astray. Fortunately, the common school, District School No. 3, was in the center of Adrian, next to the community Protestant church and within whistling distance of the McNamara residence. Thomas later recalled in verse Adrian's "chapel and schoolhouse upon the green mound." The school had sessions in summer as well as winter (no doubt to the relief of Mrs. McNamara); but the schoolday classes ended in mid-afternoon, with daylight to spare. Tom recalled the joys of dismissal in the same nostalgic doggerel: "The stern visaged master, each morning we greet/Our voices to cheers and hurrahs that ascend/At close of school hours we most earnestly lend...." I suppose that the parents designated some chores to fill in a portion of the free time, but there was still plenty of opportunity for mischief. The McNamara kids were known locally as "Pat Mac's bad boys." There must have been some grounds for the monicker.

Railroader Pat had no objection at all if his sons hung out at the little local railroad station. As a matter of fact, this proved to be an educational experience, for there the boys could learn the art of telegraphy. But Pat Mac absolutely forbade them to frequent the general store. The local men who made the store their club, and sat around the stove smoking pipes and munching soda crackers, were rough in their talk; and Pat didn't want his lads exposed to that type of education.

He was ready to enforce the ban, too. One day the older Mac boys, in a less-than-angelic mood, conspired to flout their Pa's command. They agreed to visit the forbidden place all together, persuaded that in union there is strength. But in a small town, news can travel like wildfire; and the mutineers had scarcely crossed the forbidden threshold when Patrick McNamara was told of the mutiny. He strode at once to the store, caught the culprits red-handed, and ordered them outside. Then he snatched up the first stick he could find by the roadside and thrashed them equally all the way home.

There was no second conspiracy.

Guarding their children from coarse talk was not the only problem that Patrick and Frances McNamara had to face as they tried to raise their family in a strong Catholic faith. The parents could and did teach their youngsters prayers and catechism, but they no doubt wished that they were a little closer than nine miles to the nearest parish church, St. Ann's in Hornell.

Mr. and Mrs. McNamara were nevertheless intent on schooling the kids in their duty of weekly attendance at Mass. Come Sunday, the whole family, dressed in their best, went to the Adrian railroad station and hoisted a handcar on the tracks. Father put Mother into the best place and tucked her in. Then the Mac menfolk, working in shifts, pumped the nine miles to Hornellsville. Since Pat knew the regular train schedules, they normally had an open track for the trip. One Sunday, however, they suddenly heard a train steaming up behind them. They all jumped off and derailed the handcar in the nick of time. When the unexpected train had passed, they set the handcar once more on the rails, and pumped on to their destination. Every Sunday after Mass, Mrs. Mac did her weekly shopping in Hornellsville. Apparently she had reached an agreement with a storekeeper to open his shop for her on Sunday as a personal favor. After she had made her purchases, the family boarded the handcar again, hugging their packages of groceries, and pumped merrily home.

Let's focus now on Thomas Alexander. I don't know how much schooling his father had, but it is quite clear that Patrick encouraged his children, especially the boys, to acquire as good an education as they could manage. Of course they had to pay their own way: there was no room for tuition in a foreman's budget. They heeded his advice.

When the Mac kids were growing up, the New York State public school system had not yet come into being; but even in rural districts one could usually find reputable private academies. After finishing his course at the district school, Tom enrolled in the academy at Canisteo, New York, four miles from home. Incorporated under the New York State Board of Regents in 1868, Canisteo Academy had opened in 1871 in a new and well-equipped building. Tom, now fifteen, entered the following spring and spent most of the year there, apparently even the summer session. Canisteo was on the Erie line, so he probably traveled to and from school on a family pass.

By the end of summer his funds had run out. It was up to him to find a job that would pay for future schooling. The job he landed was that of telegrapher in the little Erie station at Adrian.

He had been working up to this position for some months by serving as a part-time telegrapher. A telegrapher at Adrian was certainly not the busiest of all telegraphers on the Erie line, so Thomas had enough spare time at work for studying and knitting his own socks. However isolated his occupation may have been, there was one period of broader excitement that he never forgot: the events surrounding the assassination of a leading Erie Railroad official, Jim Fisk.

Scandals have marred the careers of more than one American president. In the 1900's, Warren Harding had his Teapot Dome and Richard Nixon had his Watergate. In the 1800s, Ulysses S. Grant became entangled in the web of piracy spun by the "robber barons" of that age. The most melodramatic of these national speculators was James Fisk, Jr. (1834-1872).

Fisk had little education but great financial daring and limitless gall. In 1869 he, Jay Gould, and others, had boldly attempted to corner the national gold market, and even to implicate President Grant in their conspiracy. Fortunately, the United States Treasury was able to head them off. But the peak date of their plot, September 24, 1869, was still called "Black Friday," because their intrigue severely jolted the American economy and ruined hundreds of investors. Fisk came out of it unscathed by completely repudiating contracts he had made involving millions of dollars. When a Congressional committee asked him what had happened to the money, he simply said that it had "gone where the woodbine twineth."

Around the same time as the gold conspiracy, Fisk had won a battle against Cornelius Vanderbilt, master of the New York Central, to take over the Erie Railroad. Jim became king of the Erie, however, not to improve but to despoil it. Nevertheless, this brilliant, irresponsible, high-living, friendless adventurer was doomed to self-destruction. On January 6, 1872, Fisk was shot to death in a New York hotel by a business partner, Edward

Stokes, who was as unscrupulous as Jim and in love with Jim's woman. Telegraphers soon clicked out the news along the wires of the nation: "Stokes shoots Fisk!" Young Tom, sitting in the Adrian station, could scarcely believe the message that beeped out of the receiver. It was this teenager's first contact with major crime and scandal. Especially in Erie Railroad circles, the excitement continued for some time, and during the period of mourning, the trains that swept by the Adrian station were festooned with the crepe of official, if not necessarily heartfelt, mourning for the reckless Erie director.

By the spring of 1874, Tom had earned enough as telegrapher to renew his high school studies. Instead of returning to Canisteo, however, he decided to try Alfred Academy. Alfred Academy had been incorporated in 1842 by a group of Seventh Day Baptists. Alfred University, founded in 1857, had grown out of this school. Both the University and the Academy were located at Alfred, a village in Allegany County. It was some eighteen miles west of Adrian, but still on the Erie line.

Alfred Academy did not measure up to Tom's expectations, so he spent only the spring and summer terms there. In the fall of 1874, he tried still a third high school in the area, Woodhull Academy. Woodhull, too, was in Steuben County, some twenty miles southeast of Adrian. The Academy, established in 1868, was considered a superior secondary school. It had a student body of two hundred boys and girls from the vicinity – almost as many as the whole population of Woodhull village. This time, Thomas was attending a school not on the Erie railroad line, so he had to live at Woodhull during the week, returning home only on weekends and vacations. The Academy had a special residence for the dozen or so girl-students from out-of-town. Boys from a distance lived with local families, doing chores to pay for bed and board. The new student from Adrian was enrolled at Woodhull Academy from Fall 1874 through June 1875. His high school career was now finished, and he was eighteen-going-on-nineteen.

But Tom was not ready to call a halt to schooling. High school had only whetted his appetite for further study, and he was now determined to go on to college. Of course, that meant more time out in which to collect the funds. This time he decided to take up teaching. (The qualifications for teachers in rural schools were not very high in those days.) He learned the ropes that summer by serving as schoolmaster in his original Alma Mater, District School No. 3 at Adrian. During the following school year, 1875-1876, he taught in the elementary school at Rexville, a dozen miles south of Canisteo. He must have felt as much at home in Rexville as in Adrian, for there were many Irish Catholics in the Rexville neighborhood, including kinsfolk on both the McNamara and the McMullen sides.

By the fall of 1876, Tom's savings were large enough to cover college tuition. So in September he hugged and kissed the family goodbye and set out on his longest journey yet. The college of his choice was at Suspension Bridge, a suburb of Niagara Falls, New York; its name was the College and Seminary of Our Lady of Angels. Since 1883 the school has been called Niagara University. Priests of the Congregation of the Mission (the Vincentian Fathers) founded it in 1856 on a site downstream from the great Niagara cataract. The primary aim of the Vincentians was to train young men for the priesthood, but they also welcomed to their college department those who intended to remain laymen, or who at least had not decided on their life calling.

From September 1876 to June 1879 the name of Thomas Alexander McNamara stood in the list of the Niagara collegians. Although Our Lady of Angels could award the degree of bachelor of arts, Tom left before he had completed the full four years of the degrees course.

Niagara was a small school in his day. The student body numbered 113 when he entered, and in his last year it was down to 78. Students were charged the rather odd sum of $131 per semester. This covered tuition, room and board, washing and mending. There was an extra fee of $2 a term for "Vocal Music." Tom signed up for it, but only in the first year. If the collegians wanted music lessons in organ or piano, they had to pay an additional

$60. Lessons in violin, flute or clarinet were less – only $40. (The school provided the instruments, on loan.) Thomas's funds were too low to cover instrumental lessons. Like the rest of his peers, he had to buy his own textbooks, but these cost no more than a dollar or two apiece. Beyond tuition and texts, and an occasional bit of medicine, his only other expenditures, according to the school records, were a slate for erasable notes and computations, and a fat sheaf of "foolscap" paper – the large sheets customarily used in the schools of the era.

The Vincentian teaching staff at Niagara was a small group of priests, each of whom usually taught more than one subject. As in most liberal arts colleges of those days, there was a heavy emphasis on classical literature and a good deal of Latin and Greek composition as well as reading. English composition and "declamation" were also taught. History was not neglected. The courses in mathematics ran from algebra through calculus; but science was under-represented. The only scientific course was astronomy. Naturally, there was a class in the Catholic religion. It was listed simply as "Catechism," but it surely went deeper than the brief questions and answers of the "penny catechism."

When a school satisfied Tom, he studied diligently. This had been verified in his high-school career. He seems to have been pleased, then, with what Niagara had to offer, for he showed himself a better-than-average student. At each year's commencement, he was listed on the honor roll. He got first or second honorable mention in Algebra I, History II, Declamation II, Catechism II, Astronomy, English Composition, Virgil, Livy, and Latin Composition. His highest honors were a second premium in Trigonometry II, and a first premium in Differential Calculus. One of his chief rivals in the ratings was James Bustin. James was to go on to the priesthood, and, years afterward, to become Dr. McNamara's energetic pastor in Corning.

Whatever the quality of instruction at Our Lady of Angels, it gave Thomas a rather broad educational base, and an incentive to continuing study. The courses in Latin and English composition taught him the fundamentals of writing, and the course in declamation prepared him to feel at ease before an adult audience.

There can be no doubt, furthermore, that he profited by the religious instruction as one who had thus far never attended a Catholic school. He also took in stride the almost monastic rule of life imposed on the Niagara students whether or not they intended to go on for the priesthood.

It certainly was a strict regime judged from today's perspective. Smoking was forbidden. Expulsion was the penalty for possession or use of intoxicants. Students could not even leave the grounds without permission. Three times a week there was a "military drill" and "inspection of attire."

There was also a quasi-monastic program of religious devotions which both seminarians and secular students were required to attend. The day started with community morning prayers, meditation and Mass. Some time during the day there was a community recitation of the rosary. Each collegian was expected to receive the sacraments of Penance and Holy Eucharist at least every two weeks. General Communion was scheduled on major Church feasts, which the Fathers observed with full solemnity. Night prayers in common concluded the day's activities. Then the "great silence" took over, ending only after breakfast on the following day.

Thomas McNamara derived permanent benefit from both the liberal arts and religious studies at Niagara, and its devotional regime. It confirmed in him the manly piety that he had learned from his parents – a piety which, as we shall see, was an important facet of his medical personality. Praying the rosary, reading the Bible, avoiding profanity or coarse language, were to remain lifelong habits. So, too, were the little devotional practices that certainly dated from his youth. "Mary, pray for us!" came from his lips as easily as a sigh. When he was about to read something aloud from a newspaper, he would first whisper a little prayer and then strike his breast with the knuckle of his thumb. Sometimes, too, in the course of his usually animated conversation, he would trace the sign of the cross on his knee with his thumbnail. Only those close to him realized that these were devout practices. He never paraded them; indeed, they became so much a part of his naturally nervous behavior that he was not always conscious of them.

All this suggests the question, had Tom chosen Niagara with the thought of going on for the priesthood? His mother may have seen it as a possibility; but neither she nor Patrick pried unasked into his thoughts or intruded on his decision. In June 1879, Thomas himself put an end to any conjecture, by leaving Niagara for good. If not the priesthood, what then? Medicine.

Tom got the idea from his brother Dan. Dan, like Tom, had gone to Canisteo Academy and Alfred Academy, financing his highschooling as a telegrapher. After high school he tried his hand as a salesman. In 1879, however, he arranged with Dr. Joseph Robinson, a Hornell physician, to enter his office and study medicine. In the old days, many an American lawyer never attended a law school, but "read law" in a lawyer's office, and then took the State bar examinations. A good many early American physicians also learned their profession by "reading medicine" with a medical doctor. "Reading medicine" was on the wane, however, after the middle of the nineteenth century, and by 1859 there were eight medical colleges in New York State alone. It was quite likely "Doc Joe" himself who recommended to the oldest of the Mac boys that he matriculate in the medical school of New York University. Robinson himself was an alumnus of Buffalo Medical College, but he had done postgraduate work in New York City at Bellevue Hospital, which was closely associated with the New York University medical department. Dan took Dr. Robinson's advice. So did Tom. They agreed to go to New York in the autumn of 1880. The McNamaras of Adrian were about to become a medical family.

How would Tom finance this professional education? By going back to the school room. He signed up for the year 1879-1880 as a public school teacher in Rathboneville (now Rathbone) on the Erie Railroad some fourteen miles east of Adrian.

The new "professor" at Rathboneville was not the callow

eighteen year-old of skimpy academic background who had served as Adrian's schoolmaster in 1875. He was now close to twenty-three, and had three years of college to his credit. But neither venerable age nor vast knowledge can fully protect a teacher from the pranks of his students. As Tom certainly remembered, school kids throughout history have always been happier to leave the schoolhouse than to enter it.

One winter night in 1880, the Rathbone scholars carried out an absolutely classic plot to get a holiday. Breaking into the school after dark, they detached the pipe from the stove, the only source of heat in the building; laboriously toted the stove itself to a frozen pond across the street; and dropped it triumphantly through a hole in the ice. When Schoolmaster McNamara entered the freezing schoolroom next morning, he naturally had to suspend classes until the heating problem could be solved.

Doctor Tom used to chuckle in later life at the ingenuity of his Rathbone pupils. But the winter of 1880 had its sad recollection, too. The McNamara children suddenly lost their mother in January. The whole family had been together for Christmas, 1879, and when they scattered after the holidays everything seemed all right at home. On January third Frances McNamara suffered a severe attack of her chronic ailment, asthma, and died at the age of forty-nine. Her children returned home for the funeral. The sad rite took place at St. Ann's Church in Hornell, and burial was in the parish cemetery. All who had known her grieved. She had been a wise woman and a friend in need.

Fannie McNamara's death marked the end of an epoch for the McNamara family. Except for Patrick – "Pack" – who was fifteen, the children she had borne and raised were grown up and on their own. Later on – perhaps at retirement – Patrick Senior even gave up his little homestead beside the tracks at Adrian and moved to Hornell. There, on Mill Street, he built a new home for himself, Pack, his two daughters (as yet unmarried), and whoever else of the family happened around. Patrick built a couple more houses as investments, becoming a sort of minor capitalist. The immigrant youth from County Limerick had achieved a modest prosperity, and his family had grown up naturally American.

Patrick McNamara and Frances McMullen had been good parents. They had taught their children ambition and industry, but also sound values; frugality without stinginess; piety without hypocrisy. Most of all, they had raised them lovingly, and their sons and daughters remained, for the most part, close to each other thereafter. The Mac boys and girls were not saints, but they never forgot the basic lessons their parents had instilled into them.

The girls married rather late, but happily. Young Fannie became the wife of William McCarthy, a pleasant grocer of Blossburg, in northern Pennsylvania. After her husband died in 1918, she and her unmarried daughter Frances moved to Camden, New Jersey, to be near her sons Arthur and William. "Peacock Mary" marched to the altar with John L. Shannon, a jolly and competent insurance agent. They lived in Corning for several years, and then moved to Camden, New Jersey, where "J. L." rose into a high executive position. John and Mary would have made fond parents, but unfortunately they never had children.

The later careers of the "Pat Mac's bad boys" were even more interesting. When Dan and Tom came home with their medical degrees, the other three brothers began thinking along the same line. Alec, after several years of peddling farm produce and a couple of years of selling shoes, entered the medical school of the University of Buffalo, receiving his doctor's degree in 1887. He practiced medicine for two years in Rochester, New York; then transferred to Lockport, New York, where he continued medical work until his death in 1941. The baby of the family, Pack, also attended the Buffalo medical school. (He enrolled under the name Patterson McNamara.) On graduation in 1889, he opened his office at Seneca Falls, New York. A year later, however, when he married Mollie Desmond of Seneca Falls, with Dr. Tom as the best man, he was once more signing himself "Patrick." Had lovely, sensible Mollie brought him around? Unfortunately, Pack died unexpectedly in 1895 on a visit to Hornell, at the age of only twenty-nine. He and Mollie had no children.

The remaining brother, William, also went to medical school. However, his asthma prevented him from continuing in medicine. Seeking relief in a higher altitude, he moved to Pueblo, Colorado. A handsome and gracious man, genuinely gifted as a mathematician, he rose to paymaster of the American Smelting and Refining Works. He also entered local politics and was elected county treasurer.

His wife, Eleanor Pearsall, an Owego girl of Alabama gentry descent, bore him three girls and two boys. But since his illness grew worse in Pueblo, he returned east and died in Corning in 1917. If Will's own medical aspirations were unfulfilled, his son Alexander won an M.D. many years later. As we shall see, Tom's son Thomas Leo, also entered the medical profession. So did Arthur, the son of Fannie McNamara McCarthy.

Today historians are much interested in the "upward mobility" of our immigrant forefathers. That is, the successful efforts on the part of immigrants of every background to encourage their American-born children to climb higher than themselves on the ladder of achievement. Was this not why they had come to the land of opportunity?

It seems to me that these scholars could find much to interest them in the case of Patrick McNamara from Ballycahane. A humble railroader, who settled, not in the self-conscious "Little Ireland" of some big American city but in the quiet of a Yankee countryside, Patrick had the joy of seeing four of his sons embrace one of the noblest and most highly respected of human professions.

— CHAPTER TWO —

The Doctor is IN

Today's medical school graduates probably do not get so excited about receiving their diplomas as graduates did in the 1880's. Even after having passed a four-year course in medical school, they know that they still have years of internship and residency in a hospital before they can set up their own practice. Of course, the lengthened curriculum of medical studies does indicate how much the science of medicine progressed in the last century. Two years used to be enough to give a "med" student the basics of his profession. Now it takes a minimum of seven years to cover the necessary ground.

Entering professional practice was also far simpler for the class of 1882. No internship was required, no residency was prescribed. Once you had the sheepskin you bought the shingle, nailed it up outside an office, and began to apply to suffering mankind the remedies you had been taught.

The main decision that faced Dr. Dan and Dr. Tom after graduation was where to nail up the shingle. Dan first chose Batavia, New York, although he later transferred to Binghamton, and ended up in Utica.

Tom found it harder to make up his mind. He first thought of going to St. Mary's, Pennsylvania. What prompted the thought, I don't know. St. Mary's is in Elk County, northwestern Pennsylvania. It is some eighty air miles southeast of Adrian, New York; but the circuitous route by train would have been much longer. In the early 1880's, the borough and township of St. Mary's had no more than 1,500 inhabitants. Settled in 1842 by German Catholics who had first immigrated to Philadelphia and Baltimore, it had retained its largely German character despite a later influx of Irish families. The high, uneven terrain of the country made farming difficult, so lumbering and woodworking, and later on, mining, became the isolated town's chief industries.

According to family tradition, Dr. Tom went down to St. Mary's soon after graduation. However, he decided rather quickly that he would not be happy there; so he packed his valise and came back home after the briefest of stays. The reasons for his return are as obscure as the reasons for his going. All right; but where should he launch his career if not at St. Mary's?

In this dilemma, Tom decided to visit Aunt Mary in Corning, New York. She had a lot of common sense, and might have some good advice. Mary McNamara of Hornellsville was a sister of Patrick McNamara's. She had married Thomas Kennedy, an employee of the Fall Brook Railroad. Since Corning was the center of operations of that small north-and-south-running railway line, the Kennedys had settled in Corning. Mary was almost the same age as Tom McNamara's own mother, and her six living children were almost parallel in age with Tom's brothers and sisters. Three of them were girls: Annie, Mary and Jo. After the death of Frances McNamara, Dr. Tom looked on Aunt Mary Kennedy as a second mother. She was not only sensible but a lot of fun, and the whole Kennedy family reflected her good cheer. A visit to Aunt Mary also had a fringe benefit: she made wonderful apple pie.

The visit paid off. Tom decided to settle in Corning village itself, where the physicians numbered only a half dozen. If Mary Kennedy had not been the first to suggest such a solution, she would surely have been delighted by his choice.

All things considered, it was a good choice. Real estate speculators had established Corning in 1835 on the south side of the
Chemung River, a northwestern tributary of the Susquehanna
River system. Situated at the head of the Chemung Canal Feeder,
this little town was a promising canal port for the trans-shipment
of local lumber and the soft coal mined in the district of
Blossburg, Pennsylvania. By 1846, 1,700 people had settled on
the Corning side of the Chemung, and new streets were being
laid out up the slopes of its southern hills. In 1848 the village
secured incorporation.

Having begun as an ambitious little port town, Corning gradually developed into an ambitious little industrial city. In 1851
the New York and Erie Railroad was completed, connecting the
shores of the Hudson River opposite New York City with the
shores of Lake Erie. The tracks had been laid through Corning in
1850, right down the center of the village at grade level – an
inconvenient and often dangerous routing that it took a century
to alter. Inconvenient or not, the Erie provided Corning and all
the southern tier of counties with a more direct access to New
York City. In 1881 the construction of a second State-wide railway, the Delaware, Lackwanna and Western, reached Corning in
its western progress. This, too, originated in the New York City
area. Even the Fall Brook Railroad, which during the 1870's and
1880's extended its mileage south to Williamsport,
Pennsylvania, and north to Lyons, New York, was to link
Corning roundaboutly with New York in 1899, when it was taken
over by the New York Central as its Pennsylvania Division.
Corning's nexus with New York City certainly played some part
in inducing the Brooklyn firm that became the Corning Glass
Works to move there in 1868. With the Glass Works came the
first of a number of those affiliated cut glass factories that ultimately won for Corning the nickname, "The Crystal City."
Industrialization promoted faster growth in the village. By 1880
the population had risen to 4,803. Ten years later, Corning village, joined by Knoxville, the unincorporated hamlet on the
more spacious north side of the valley, would incorporate as

Corning city, with 8,583 citizens. At the peak of its growth the municipality would never exceed twice that population, but it remained wholesome and imaginative.

Corning's continuing growth made it even better for a new physician. Its increasing body of Catholic citizens was an added incentive for a Catholic medic. Most of them were Irish, but there were some Portuguese and Poles, a good many Germans, and the pioneers of what would later become a large colony of Italians. Since 1849 the Catholics of Corning and vicinity had had a church of their own, St. Mary's, on that shoulder of Higman Hill familiarly known as "Irish Hill." Before 1882, it seems, no Catholic physician had practiced in Corning. One who settled there would surely be welcomed by St. Mary's parishioners.

The die was cast. In May 1882 Thomas Alexander McNamara, the new doctor in town, hung up his shingle at the entrance of the Concert Block, a building centrally located on the "village square." The Concert Block was a brick commercial and professional building whose third floor had served for thirty years as a hall for lectures and entertainments. Perhaps the best known of those who had appeared on its stage was "The Original Gen. Tom Thumb." The famous midget visited Corning in 1856. Doctor Mac rented two rooms on the back, alley-side of the second floor–one room to serve as an office, the other as a bedroom.

I suppose that back in 1856 large crowds had climbed to the third floor of the Concert Block to pay their half-dimes, dimes and quarters for the privilege of meeting Tom Thumb. In 1882, for an agonizingly long time, nobody climbed to the second floor to seek the services of the novice doctor.

One day, however, Dr. McNamara heard a knock. He opened the office door and beheld a man unknown to him. It was his first patient.

It is hard to say who was the more nervous as the sick man sat down face to face with the physician. Probably the physician. Here is the "dialogue" that followed, as the Doctor loved to repeat it in later (and more secure) decades.

"Let me feel your pulse" said Doctor Mac. The patient proffered his wrist.

"Hmmm. Let me see your tongue." The patient stuck out his tongue.

"Hmmm. Let me feel your pulse again." The patient obliged.

"Let me see your tongue." Out came the tongue.

"Hmmm!   Let me feel your tongue…"

If the interview had ended with the sudden and tragic death of the ailing man, my father would surely never have told the story at all. So he must have been able to suggest some remedy that satisfied Patient No. 1, and perhaps even cured him. The encounter may have been an ordeal for the physician, but at least he was in business.

If Doctor Mac, a man of nervous energy, found the relative inactivity of these first months hard to bear, at least he knew that the Kennedys were rooting for him. He boarded with Aunt Mary and found the company of his cousins a good tonic. Though he never had much interest in card playing, on slack weekends he may have sat in on the Saturday evening Kennedy poker game. Everybody played, and more often than not Aunt Mary vanquished her men folk. Doctor Tom also rolled and cut his pills in the Kennedy kitchen, and Cousin Annie Kennedy was honored to help him.

The new Corning doctor, as a practitioner of general medicine, had to be a "specialist in everything": internal medicine, obstetrics, surgery, bone-setting. As time passed, therefore, he gradually acquired a clientele composed of people burdened with a variety of medical problems. He also sought and won election in 1884 as a Steuben County coroner. The term was three years. He ran again for the office in 1890, and won another (non-consecutive) term. Being a coroner was good for both his purse and his public relations.

Around January 1885, Doc was named a resident surgeon of the Erie Railroad – another salaried position. Family and personal associations with the Erie must have counted when he won that post. He and Dr. Henry C. May shared the local Erie surgical work.

Railroad surgery involved a good many emergency accident

cases. For instance, one day when Mason B. Coger, a Corning youngster, (1876-1964), was passing by the Erie baggage room, he noticed that something unusual was going on inside. With boyish curiosity he wormed his way through the crowd within to see what the attraction was. A man had suffered an injury in an Erie accident, and Doctor Mac was busy amputating his leg. This was long before the days of aseptic surgery, so the scene in that freight room was pretty gory. Young Coger (as he told me years afterward) felt an uncontrollable need for fresh air, and got out as fast as he could.

In 1888, another railroading tragedy struck closer to home. Aunt Mary's son, John Kennedy, three years younger than the Doctor, worked for the Fall Brook Railroad. In November of that year John suffered a similar leg injury, and the Fall Brook surgeon performed a similar amputation. As soon as Doctor Tom heard of the casualty, he took a train to where his cousin lay. By the time he arrived, however, John was dead. This was the second shock that Aunt Mary had experienced within a single year. Her son Tom had died the previous March, at the age of only twenty-five. A grave depression now seized this normally happy woman. Grief may have contributed to her death only two years later, at the age of fifty-nine. Doctor Tom was a source of strength to the Kennedy family during these two years of trial. He was especially saddened by the death of his aunt. It was like losing his own mother twice.

But the role of railroad physician also had its joyous moments. On January 29, 1885, another Erie casualty called the Doctor to Big Flats, some nine miles east of Corning. While he was there, Annie Purcell, the wife of Tobias Purcell, an Erie engineer, sensed that her new baby was about to arrive. Learning where Doctor Mac was, Toby borrowed a switch engine from the Corning yards and sped down to the Flats. When he arrived and located the Doctor, he cried out: "Leave the dead, and give a little attention to the living!" So Doc climbed into the cab of the engine and the two sped back to the Erie yards and to the Purcell home on "Windy Row." That same day Annie gave birth to

Philip, her bouncing first-born.

My father seems to have liked railroad medical work, perhaps because railroading was in his blood. I am not sure how long he continued in the employ of the Erie; but in the 1890's he was appointed resident surgeon for the Fall Brook Railroad. He held this office until 1899, when the Fall Brook line was absorbed by the New York Central.

The wider his practice grew, the more convinced he became that it had been wise to settle in Corning. As a matter of fact, as early as July 8, 1885, he even ventured to get married to a local girl – a further commitment to the Crystal City.

I don't know where he first met the girl of his dreams – perhaps at some parish doing, perhaps in connection with his profession. She was Katherine Dwyer, the daughter of Thomas Dwyer of Erie Avenue.

Tom Dwyer was a native of Pallas Grean in County Limerick. He came to the States in 1850, worked for ten years as a grocer in Warsaw, New York, and then opened a grocery store in Corning in partnership with Morris Fitzgerald. Gentle, well educated (largely by himself), and a business man of integrity, he quickly won the respect of Corningites and became not only a leading figure in the Catholic community but the holder of several appointive and elective offices in the local government. Bridget O'Malley, his wife, was also a native of Ireland. She bore her husband four daughters: Maggie (1860), Kate (1863), Nell (1867), and Fannie (1876). Although it was not customary in those days for girls to seek higher education, Tom Dwyer encouraged his daughters to improve their minds by reading, and to become interested in politics. Kate was apparently the most studious of the girls. For three years she was a teacher in Public School No. 2. Katherine was also the prettiest of the Dwyers. She had dark brown hair, a gently molded oval face, and light blue eyes that were at the same time innocent and frank. Furthermore, she was as capable as she was pretty.

I say Tom "ventured" to marry Kate. His earnings were still slim, and the newlyweds had to economize carefully in the early years together. First they rented rooms on Cedar Street, a couple of blocks from his office. Not long afterward, Thomas Dwyer built a new house for his own family next to his original residence on Erie Avenue, and divided the old residence into two apartments. The Doctor and Kate took one of these apartments. The other was occupied by Maggie Dwyer and her husband, John Daniel McGannon, a railroad conductor whom she had married in 1884. Tom and Kate's first child was born in the Erie Avenue apartment. They named him Adrian Alexander McNamara. The baby's second name, like the second name of his father, came from Great-Grandfather McMullen. "Adrian" can only have been picked as a fond allusion to the Doctor's home town, although it is also the name of a saint.

Early in 1888, Tom and Kate embarked on a new housing adventure. They bought a house of their own at 32 East First Street, to serve as both residence and office. This building would remain the family home until 1969. Barney Cahill – "an Irishman with an English accent," and an expert glassblower – had built it in 1872. It was designed in the "Italianate" style with a low-pitched pyramidal roof and wide eaves "supported" by carpentered brackets. The location was central and ideal for both home and professional purposes. It cost a lot – $4,500. The new purchaser also had to build a full front porch to provide access both to the double black-walnut-and-glass door of the residence and the adjacent door to the office. The office door, a new one, was hung in the former east bay of the front bay window. It was some years before the Mac couple could pay off the costs of building and improvements. Part of this economy was to rent three upstairs rooms, use the back parlor as a bedroom, and leave the dining room unfurnished.

The office was typical of the medical offices of old-time general practitioners, and would serve Doc Mac for almost forty years. There was no question which front door was the entrance to the office. Its glass window pane bore the word "OFFICE" in large white enamel letters. Below the arched pane of glass there was a twist-bell that rattled more than rang, but did have a commanding voice. When a patient entered this door, his eyes took in a single room no larger than fifteen by eighteen feet with a hardwood floor carpeted by an Axminster rug. Neither then nor later was there an official waiting room. Waiting patients sat in the dining room which lay behind the sliding double door at the rear; or on the steps of the hall stairway of the house; or, in warmer weather, on the front porch.

The office appointments were mainly of oak. The windows had inside oaken shutters for greater privacy. A modern oak grandfather clock stood just to the left of the entrance. An oak desk – roll top, of course – was against the left wall past the hall-way door. It was provided with an oaken swivel chair and brass goose-neck lamp, and surmounted by an oil painting of a quaint old Italian couple seated at table – an inadequate copy of an unimportant picture. (The painting's only medical significance was that it was the work and gift of a local physician's wife.) To the right of the painting, but a bit lower on this wall, was a framed photo of Dr. John B. Murphy, a noted Chicago surgeon. Across the far left corner was a chimney wall with a fireplace framed by a mantel of handsome black marble. It was accommodated for a gas burner, but was never actually used for heating. Above the mantel hung the doctoral diploma, limp and rippled in its black walnut frame. Below and to the right of the diploma, hanging by a hook, was a plaster-of-Paris head of an Arab in high relief. His face had dark, desert-browned skin and his teeth were gleaming white, but his facial expression was more romantic than fierce. (At least he didn't scare me as a child. I enjoyed sticking my finger into his eyes and mouth.)

On the right side of the office, suspended over the radiator, was a sepia print of "The Doctor," a painting by the English Victorian artist Luke Fildes. The picture showed a bearded physician watching intently beside the makeshift cot of a sleeping sick girl. The grieving parents stood by, sad but helpless, in the shadows to the right. Years ago this picture was often reproduced in medical contexts. What made it an item of special interest here was that Fildes's physician closely resembled Doctor

Mac in his "full-beard" period (1900-1905 ?).

Further south along the right wall of the room, past the west window, were two oaken cases; a glass case containing a micro-scope and an assortment of frightening surgical instruments; and an oaken bookcase with a built-in desk, a set of warped drawers with brass pulls, and several rows of medical books. Along the top of both instrument case and bookcase were ranged rows of bottles filled with pills of great variety (no longer confected in the kitchen). Rhubarb and ipecac, for example; migraine tablets; heroin; cascara sagrada; asafetida (smelling like rotting garlic!); Brown's Mixture, for coughs (delicious!). The other major fur-nishing of the room was an iron throne at right center, painted black and equipped with cushions of imitation leather. With a twist of the lever, this "throne" could be extended fore and aft to become a table for examinations, operations, and deliveries. By the time I became acquainted with this aging medical equipment after 1910, Corning had a hospital, and the Doctor performed most of his surgery there. But he still might do minor surgery, like removing cinders from the eye or lancing boils or even cut-ting out tonsils, in the office or, weather permitting, on the front or back porch.

Finally, the whole medical office was illuminated by a hang-ing chandelier equipped with both electrical and gas fixtures. The gas fixtures were seldom used, but did come in handy when a thunderstorm caused an electrical blackout.

As late as 1925, when most Corning physicians had no office hours on Sunday and on one or more weekdays, Doctor Mac continued to advertise his availability every day, from 2:00 to 4:00 and 7:00 to 8:00 P.M. Of course, he knew that people would usually not come on Sunday, except in an emergency.

Most of the old-time general practitioners spent at least as much time on house calls as they did on office service. Since there was no schedule of hours for house visits, the doctors were within reach at any hour of the day or night.

The "speaking tube" at 32 East First Street was a symbol of this availability. It was located alongside the polished black-on-brass sign "T. A. McNamara, M.D." which was attached to the clapboards between the front door and the office door. The tube was a 1½-inch intercom pipe that extended from the front porch up to the hall doorway of the master bedroom. Its mouthpiece was equipped with a hinged metal whistle. Whoever came at night to summon the Doctor would first hold the whistling disk close to the opening, and blow. The shrill sound would awaken the Doctor, a light sleeper anyhow, and he would come to the upper end to answer. The visitor would then swing the whistle aside on its crank and speak his piece. "All right," the Doctor would reply, "I'll be down in a moment." He would pull on his clothing, don his hat, stop in the office to pick up his medicine case, with its stethoscope, vials of pills, and other essential equipment, and set off on his errand of mercy,

The speaking tube was less used when more Corningites subscribed to the two local telephone lines, the Century (Federal) and the Bell, which absorbed the Federal in 1919. Doctor Mac's Bell number was easy to remember: 123.

I am not quite sure how my father traveled to his patients in the beginning. Could he have afforded to rent, or much less, to purchase, a horse and buggy in those earliest Corning years? If not, he must have done a lot of walking. Of course, there were times later on when shanks' mare was the only way of getting places. As late as February 17, 1903, when Helen Cronin McMillen's baby was due, Doc had to plow through knee-deep snow to reach his destination. Now, it is true that the McMillens lived only three blocks away, but there was no winter wind more wild than the one you encountered when slogging up Irish Hill. For self-protection, on the most arctic days I used to walk backward much of the way to school.

When rural patients from the other side of Spencer Hill or from down Caton way needed the Doctor in snowy weather, they usually sent a driver to pick him up in a sleigh, or a bobsled. Sometimes even in a box! On one occasion, the country drifts were so deep that the driver drove his horse right over the top of the fence before he realized he was off the road. If the Doctor arrived at a farmhouse after dusk, and infant delivery or an emergency operation was in order, he would do his work in the light of the massed kerosene lamps of the household.

During the mid-1890's, Doc made some of his calls on a primitive bicycle with wooden spokes and hard-rubber tires. But by that time he had apparently also acquired his own horse, carriage and cutter, and by 1900 he had built a small barn on the alley to house all three.

The first McNamara horse was Dan, a nice, slick sorrel. Dan was succeeded by Ned, a brown horse. In his youth, Ned had won a reputation as a race horse. Doctor Mac bought him on a tip from Dr. George Lane, one of his colleagues. Ned adapted perfectly to his second career. He was gentle and so dependable that he knew his master's route by heart. So when the Doctor hitched him up, flicked the reins, and ordered "Giddyap," Ned would first make a bee line for the home of Mrs. Ray Young, a chronic invalid. Drawing up before her door, he would nibble the grass by the curb until the call was over. They say it was much the same when Doctor drove out the country roads that led to his regular rural clients. Ned was so sure of his destination and his own ability to reach it that the driver was even able to take a catnap along the way.

I dimly remember riding in the buggy on my Father's lap, and being permitted to hold the reins and "drive" the good old horse. I must have been very young indeed, for in June, 1913, Ned disappeared. He was put out to pasture, I guess, for he did not die until 1915. Placid Ned was replaced by a black "Model T" Ford that cost the Doctor exactly $559.41. From that time on, Dr. McNamara went about his business in an automobile, although he continued to speak of "hitching up the car." He bought Ford No. 2 in 1919 and Ford No. 3 in 1921. In 1923 he switched to a Dodge coupé. You had to crank the early Fords to start the motor; the Dodge had a "self-starter." Progress!

Doctor Mac was too nervous a man to be delicate with his automobiles. Once when he was driving a later Ford – a towering coupé – he ran into a horse and wagon at the exit of the

Chemung River bridge. The tall car toppled over, but fortunately the driver climbed out unscathed. You might say that Papa drove his Fords like a horse, and his Dodge like a Ford. If that statement over-simplifies, at least it says something about his haphazard approach to automobiling.

This history of Doc McNamara's modes of business transportation – from shanks' mare to Dodge coupé – implies that by the 1920's he had built up a practice large enough to finance any type of modest vehicle that he needed. By that date he had as many patients as any other local physician, and perhaps more. It was a diversified clientele, too: blacks and whites, rich and poor, Catholics, Protestants, Jews.

His Catholic patients were in the majority, however; although with the gradual arrival in town of a few other Catholic doctors he naturally lost any earlier "monopoly." His ledgers from 1911 on (now in Cornell University Library) list people from many national segments of the Corning Catholic population. The smaller national groups included: Portuguese, like the Comoshes, Andrades, Freitases, Costas, and Sousas; Rusins (whom Corningites called "Hungarians") like the Bablos, Serdulas, and Demyans; Poles like the Tyrazinskis, Czepanskys, and Waruneks. The German families were, of course, far more numerous: the Gaisses, Markerts, Schebs, Nitsches, Fedders, Schroeders, Schubmehls, Stengers, etc. The Irish names were innumerable; Hibernians from "Irish Hill"; from the "Lower End of Town"; from the "North Side" (in increasing number); and from elsewhere in the Corning environs.

Furthermore, the trickle of Italian immigration into Corning in the 1880's had become a flood by the time of World War I. Most of these Italians engaged in unskilled labor, initially with the railroads. The majority settled near the Erie right of way, on West Erie Avenue, or in housing on either side of the adjacent Chemung River. They often took over houses from which earlier settlers had "graduated."

Doctor Mac's medical ledgers show an increasing number of musical (if often misspelled) Italian names: Ambrosone, Astolfi,

Bamonti, Barbaro, Bavisotto, Carapella, Candelupe, Cavalier, Fratarcangelo, Grimaldi, Luffred, Miller, Mizzoni, Picarazzi, Pierri, Ruocco, Russo, Stirpe, Yorio, and so forth. Before coming to Corning, the Doctor had never really known any people from "Sunny Italy." When he met them, he fell in love with them. He picked up a few Italian phrases, incorrect, perhaps, but not incomprehensible (like *testa dolor* for headache) to use when they called at his office. Other symptoms he could learn through sign language, and he rather enjoyed the challenge of communicating with them. If words and signs didn't suffice, he could seek the aid of an interpreter. What he admired them for in particular was their sense of family solidarity, and their fondness for babies. Their complete naturalness also surprised, amused and touched him. One day, for example, he made a house visit to see how a mother was faring who had given birth the day before. He found the mother busy about the housework and the father in bed!

Yes, he developed a large following – interracial, international, ecumenical. It was also a devoted following. His patients had deep confidence in him for three reasons in particular: medical skill, dependability, and winning professional manner.

1. His medical skill.

Doctor Mac's medical course had been too brief, but experience is the best educator in any profession. Persistent medical study, sharing problems with colleagues in the medical societies, alertness to new remedies: these are all keys to wisdom in the healing arts.

Fortunately for him, during the span of his active career, 1882 – 1927, the whole medical profession began to undergo an exciting shift from "bedside" medicine to "laboratory" medicine.

The agents of this change were a growing group of brilliant lab-scientists, mostly European. Scholars like Louis Pasteur, the microbiologist; Robert Koch, the bacteriologist; Paul Ehrlich, the immunologist; Walter Reed, the sanitarian; Joseph Lord Lister, the founder of antiseptic surgery; Pierre and Marya Curie, the wonderful radiological couple. The average G.P. was not called to laboratory life, but he heartily welcomed the surge of discoveries publicized by the laboratorians.

Thomas A. McNamara went further. Locally he backed the efforts of one of the above-named scientists, Lord Lister, who had been engaged in an international campaign for antiseptic medicine.

Even in the days before germs had been "discovered," this altruistic British surgeon, distressed by the deadly infections that too often followed surgical operations everywhere, was pleading for greater cleanliness in operating rooms. His effort to counter such contamination by the subsequent use of antiseptics had won some favor for his theories by reducing deaths considerably in his Male Accident Ward at Glasgow. As experiments continued, it was found that asepsis was even more effective than antisepsis. In other words, don't wait until after the operation to apply antiseptics. Eliminate before surgery every possible source of infection. The surgeons should "scrub-up" diligently, should wear sterile gowns and rubber gloves, should use only sterilized instruments, and work in an operating room as free as possible from contaminants.

Does this sound familiar? Of course it does. Asepsis describes the "scrub-up" surgical practices as we know them today, especially as depicted in TV "hospital" shows. It is hard to believe that the "ten commandments" of sanitary surgery are barely a century old!

Intrigued by Lister's compassion, Dr. McNamara became one of his faithful disciples in Corning and was ready to test the Listeran recommendations in Corning Hospital, especially regarding appendectomies and Caesarean deliveries.

In or before 1910, he performed an appendix operation, which the Corning *Leader* believed to be the first in local history. The newspaper gave few details, but the very success of the surgery suggests that in it McNamara had observed the rules of aseptic surgery.

The *Leader* paid fuller attention in 1913 when Dr. McNamara, assisted by three other surgeons, delivered Mrs. Martin Stenger of "Little Joe," a "splendidly developed boy," by Caesarean section. This was only the second such delivery in Corning's surgical annals. The *Leader* article pointed out that obstetricians had long been timid about surgical deliveries from living mothers because of the great fear of infecting the mothers themselves. "Little Joe" did not die until the 1970s. Johanna Hayer Stenger not only survived his birth without difficulty but was later delivered of two other children by the same procedure.

Shortly after his first Caesarean delivery Doctor Mac read a paper on C-sections to the Corning physicians. In his conclusion he asked whether today's doctors should have the traditional qualms about Caesarean delivery. This was his answer. "While every obstetrician or physician may not feel competent to attempt a Caesarean section, I would advise those who might hesitate not to allow the patient to die without at least making an earnest effort when expert help is not attainable." His reason? "I have every confidence in our young surgeons who understand the value of asepsis."

Did this cautious but hopeful advice perhaps even mark the victory of asepsis in Corning's medical chronicles?

When he spoke of the anonymous "young surgeons who understand the value of asepsis," Dr. Thomas Alexander McNamara had the name of one of them certainly in mind. It was his son Thomas Leo McNamara. The younger Thomas had entered Syracuse University Medical School in 1907; had won his doctorate in 1911; completed his internship at Blackwell's Island, New York Harbor, in 1913; and in the same year opened a little medical office in the Corning family home.

These were precisely the years of the asepsis controversy, and Thomas L. was happy to report to his father the course of discussion at Syracuse medical school and at the Blackwell hospital. In World War I, when T. L. was a lieutenant in the medical corps, he also kept T. A. posted on new, war-occasioned information about bone surgery. Thus the two Doctors McNamara, sharing so many talents and views in common, came to be a rather notable team.

The best witnesses to the scientific expertise of the elder McNamara were his colleagues, the physicians of Corning and vicinity. Practically all the local doctors called him in at one time or another as a consultant, particularly in cases of obstetrics, surgery and bone dislocations.

2. His dependability.

It was not just his skill alone that put patients at ease; it was his absolute dependability.

Probably the heaviest burden a doctor assumed when he became a general practitioner was that of availability to his patients, morning, noon and night. Thomas A. McNamara accepted that burden, and, being both conscientious and generous, he accepted it with good will. Sometimes this commitment required all-night vigils beside a sick bed in a private home, especially in the days before Corning Hospital was founded. The great modern antibiotics, sulfa drugs and antihistamines, were not discovered until many years after Doctor Mac's death in 1927. That usually meant round-the-clock nursing until the crisis was past.

Mrs. Thomas O'Bryan, for instance, often had serious nighttime attacks of what used to be called "acute indigestion." When she had an attack, Thomas O'Bryan and one of his older children would hurry down to 32 East First, whistle up the speaking tube, and summon the Doctor. It was usually dawn before Mrs. O'Bryan was better, so the physician breakfasted with the O'Bryan family more than once.

On another occasion a little boy on the North Side was stricken with a grave intestinal infection. Doctor diagnosed it as peritonitis. He said that the boy had only a 50-50 chance of survival, but he would do his best. He summoned Margaret Petticrew, a highly skilled Corning nurse; and physician and nurse worked throughout the dark hours to save the lad. At 6:00 A.M., the Doctor was able to assure the parents that the crisis was over.

Perhaps the saddest of these vigils were the long nights spent with children who had diphtheria. This dreadful croup paralyzed children, stopping their hearts. The Corning epidemic of 1887-1888 was particularly destructive. In some households every child died. Doctor Mac got all too accustomed to the peculiar odor that accompanied the disease. Thus, around 1915, Mrs. Anna Callahan Barrett sent for him to examine her daughter Frances who was in bed with a sore throat. As soon as he entered the house, the Doctor declared, "It's diphtheria." He had got a whiff of the "mousey" smell characteristic of the infection. Fortunately, Frances recovered. The campaign of antitoxin inoculation launched in 1913 has practically obliterated this child-killing disease in the United States. But before that time a physician could only watch the little victims carefully, hoping that they would pull through, but fully aware that the chances of survival were slim.

Medical doctors who take care of people with contagious diseases are, of course, in danger of contracting the disease themselves, or of carrying infection back to their own families. I can't recall ever having heard of this happening in the McNamara family. It may be that special guardian angels are assigned to keep physicians always immune and therefore always "IN." (On one occasion, though, my Dad did suffer from an occupational hazard. As he was operating on the infected area of a patient, the scalpel slipped and cut through his rubber glove and into his thumb. The thumb became infected and was saved only after a long battle.)

3. His winning professional manner.

The third reason for his popularity was his ideal "bedside manner." Gentle, cheerful, heartening, he talked turkey when he had to, with acceptable frankness.

Like all physicians, Doctor Mac was called on to deal with the mental as well as the physical problems of his patients. For example, in those days when narcotics were unregulated, he agonized over how to break the habit in patients who had become "hooked" through over-the-counter medication. Inevitably, too, some of his clients were hypochondriacs. At times an envelope of sugar pills was enough to drive away their "miseries." But in the case of two long-faced Corning matrons who made a hobby of feeling poorly, he took a different tack. When they called he kidded them so outlandishly that they burst out laughing in spite of themselves. Thus they forgot their ailments, at least for the time being. A joking approach also cured Mr. Harold (?) Mosher, the stove-repairman. Called to the Mosher home, the Doctor found Harold languishing in bed. After giving the patient a careful examination, he concluded that there was nothing at all wrong with him. "Well," Mosher asked, "What do you prescribe?" Doc said, "If you'd just put that big toe out from under the covers, you'd be all right." Harold, though rather surprised, accepted the prescription, got up, and was soon back at work. To the end of his life, Mr. Mosher used to laugh about his "miraculous" resurrection.

Some of the Doctor's old patients used to say of him, "He was just like one of the family." That was probably why they found his medical advice so welcome: it was like taking advice from their own fathers. Indeed, Doc Mac did not hesitate to counsel them like a father on other than medical matters – for example, on life insurance. He was personally convinced that life insurance was one of the wisest and easiest ways to save money. Therefore, especially when a young couple had their first baby, he would urge the father to take out life insurance for the long-term protection of his youngster. "You're young now," he would point out, "and the premium will be low. Invest in a policy at once, and you'll never regret it." He took special pains to recommend this practice to young Italian couples. Many parents accepted the suggestion and followed through. Still others of his clients did not hesitate to turn to him for counsel on family problems and business affairs. Whether he had all the answers doesn't matter. That they should have asked him showed that in their eyes he was a father figure.

Medical skill, dependability, and an ideal "bedside manner," were therefore three traits that won for Doctor McNamara a devoted following. But in addition to these characteristics which any good physicians would have, there was another that Doc Mac possessed in a particular way. He was a man of prayer, and if he didn't flaunt his prayerfulness, neither did he mind if it showed. For him good medicine must always be the work of a team: the Creator and the physician.

When neighbors of St. Mary's Church saw Doc park his buggy or car in front of the church at off-hours and bound up the steps, they could be pretty certain that he was going in for a "medical consultation." Dr. Stephen Collins, who started to practice medicine in Corning in the 1930's, but whose family were old-time patrons of Doctor Mac, recalled how the Doctor used to wait out the arrival of the Collins family's babies. He would walk up and down in the Collins house quietly praying the rosary.

Then there was the instance of Mrs. Savage of Hammond Street. She gave birth to a daughter, but was very ill afterward. The Doctor did not hesitate to go down on his knees beside her bed to pray for her recovery.

A frequent question was whether the newborn child would survive. If Doc thought that there was any danger that a child of Catholic parents might die before it could be taken to church for christening, he would administer emergency baptism. Not a few entries in the baptismal book of St. Mary's Church have the notation: "baptized by Dr. T.A. McNamara." There are many priests who have not baptized as often as this medical "apostle" did.

Thomas A. McNamara clearly enjoyed his profession, and all sorts of medical and surgical work. But if you should have asked him what phase of his labors he liked best, I'm sure he would have said, "Obstetrics!" He stood in awe and admiration of the mystery of parenthood. He loved children and young people, and especially enjoyed watching them at play. "All children are beautiful," he would say.

During his forty-five years of practice he brought into the world at least 4,000 babies. It was said that he never lost a child where he had been on the case from the beginning. Not that he didn't experience surprises now and then. One night, for example, after he had left a house where he had been making a call, he decided he would not go home but spend the night in the near-by home of an expectant mother whose hour was fast approaching. He asked permission to stretch out on a couch in her bedroom. Soon he fell asleep; but before long a thump awakened him. The baby had made its own debut. Jumping up, he took over from there on, and everything turned out well.

He enjoyed testing children's reactions. One day "Rilla" Costello, a friend of the McNamara daughters, dropped in at the house with her first-born, Earl Costello, Jr. About five at the time, young Earl was known to be precocious. "Can you spell cat?" Papa asked Junior. "C-a-t," he replied. "Dog?" "D-o-g," said Junior. "What kind of dog is that?" Quick as a wink. Junior answered, "Hot dog!" The Doctor was enchanted by his wit.

He studied carefully the development of the children he himself had delivered. "A child's whole character is established by the time he is twelve," he told one of his patients, Mrs. William S. Holmes. Psychologists today would push the age of personality back still farther; but Mrs. Holmes, a school teacher, kept the Doctor's comment in mind, and it proved very helpful in later years as she tried to understand the young people she was teaching. Perhaps she also learned from the Doctor another of his principles: Always encourage a child to live up to its potential.

Fascinated as he was by the great mystery of human life, Thomas McNamara considered artificial contraception, abortion and euthanasia dehumanizing. Subjects like these were first being discussed in the public forum around 1920. He took strong exception to them, and spoke his mind in a couple of public lectures, grouping them, somewhat inexactly, under the title "eugenics."

The first lecture was delivered to the Corning Academy of Medicine on February 8, 1922. Eight days later it was published in a Buffalo paper, the *Catholic Union and Times*. Since the talk dealt largely with artificial contraception, the *Union and Times* added a note that Margaret Sanger, whom it called "the Queen of Birth Control," was a native of the city in which the Doctor practiced. In the lecture itself, however, the Doctor made no mention of Mrs. Sanger.

The lecturer marshaled arguments against the eugenic viewpoint from several sources. Some of his argumentation would be considered inadequate today, and some of his remarks were unduly harsh. But he did raise certain basic questions. What does artificial contraception do, in the long run, to mother-love? Does the introduction of calculation into married love not risk turning it into a "cold proposition"? Does not the perfectly natural travail of childbearing become, in eugenicist philosophy, something tragic and therefore to be avoided? And how can eugenics hope to produce a finer race of men by mere technology, ignoring the "moral, mental and metaphysical factors" that are a part of human nature?

His audience was probably mainly medical. To them he said, at one point, "Contraception used to be spoken of behind closed doors. Now it is publicized." How they reacted I do not know. It may be that Corning medical attitudes on contraception were still conservative enough in 1922 for the Doctor to have expected majority agreement. It is equally likely that he sensed a growing attraction to "eugenic" thought among the local medical profession, and sought to counter it by pointing out its implications. If he knew his listeners would be hostile, delivery of the paper would have taken a good deal more courage. But anybody who knew Doctor Mac knew that where principles were involved, he never feared to speak out.

I imagine the second "eugenical" lecture was delivered to the same audience, soon after the first. Too bad this talk never appeared in print, for it was both milder and deeper.

In lecture No. 2, the lecturer spoke more sympathetically of those who were promoting "the new science of eugenics." He did not question the humaneness of their motivation. There is indeed much suffering in the world, and we should seek to remedy it. But in trying to do good, he cautioned, we cannot use methods that are bad.

The main fault of eugenics, as he saw it, is that the scientists have established its rules on the basis of clinical experiments rather than on the broader laws of nature. Their program includes: "artificial selection of parentage for the unborn; limitation of birth rate; sterilization for the weak, feebleminded, insane and criminal class; euthanasia or painless death for cripples, physically deformed or otherwise defective newborn infants, and the same plan of exit for those suffering from exhaustive, painful, incurable and infectious diseases." What a wonderful world this would be, he exclaimed ironically, if the program of the eugenicists should be carried into complete execution. Think of it! The human being that survived this winnowing-out would never be disturbed by anything unpleasant. "No cries of pain, sorrow and anguish will call upon his sympathies for pity; no helpless will beg for assistance; no crowds will jostle him in the battle of life; no defective, deformed or incurable, will shock his sensibilities. Life will then be but one sweet and pleasant dream."

But this "perfect world" of the eugenicists could only be achieved, he warned, through civil legislation. The implementing laws would necessarily force parents, legislators, clergymen, teachers, and, in particular, physicians and surgeons, to collaborate in a vast campaign to "denature nature."

Did he foresee Hitler's mad eugenics just a piece down the road?

The eugenic program, he concluded, is not the answer. Many physical ailments beset the human race: infant mortality, insanity, idiocy, alcoholism, tuberculosis, and various constitutional diseases. These should be dealt with, however, by attacking the social and other conditions that produce the ailments, not by liquidating the victims.

Thus spoke an experienced family physician in the 1920's, on the basis of his Hippocratic oath and four decades of experience as a medic, a father, and a counselor. Looking back across several decades of medical victories and medical treasons, we can see in his remarks something strongly prophetic.

What he opposed in his two lectures, Thomas McNamara naturally opposed in his own medical practice. He did not counsel artificial contraception. And even if he had not been backed by the laws of his Church and the current laws of the land, he would never have advised abortion.

The question of abortion did arise sometimes when unwed mothers came to see him. Understandably upset by unexpected pregnancies, they would ask how they might be rid of their unborn babies. Far from telling them how, he would give the women a gentle but persuasive little talk on the real issues at stake. In most cases, this approach proved effective. The young women were touched by his appeal to their womanhood, and a flood of tears brought them back to reality. Usually Doc would advise them to marry the father, if possible, but out of town and quietly. Whatever decision they reached on marriage, he was ready to arrange personally for these mothers to go to a facility far from Corning where they could in time be delivered of their infants at no unnecessary risk of their good name. Thus they would have the consolation of having respected their children's right to birth. Furthermore, there were always married couples – many of them childless – who would eagerly welcome little ones like these into their homes.

One fact Doc Mac learned very thoroughly in his many years of obstetrical practice: It may be difficult to feel affection for a child hidden in the womb; but a babe-in-arms has a magic way of making itself loved and wanted.

— CHAPTER THREE —

In the Public Eye

"His knowledge makes the doctor distinguished," says the Bible, "and gives him access to those in authority." (*Sirach, 38:3*)

Medical skill does merit for a physician the reverence of his community. It does give him entrée into the homes of the foremost leaders. Practically speaking, the medical profession can also be lucrative. (Who, once healed, is so thoughtless as to deny the healer his recompense?) Thus the medical doctor, achieving professional respect and sufficient means, is likely to move into the business world, and even to be called into positions of public trust.

At least the career of Thomas A. McNamara developed that way. His professional skill, his subsequent business interests and his warm, forthright personality gave evidence of leadership qualities, and gradually won for him the rank of "city father." Now, it is true that when he died in 1927, Corning proper was still a small city (15,625). But a "city father" has the same traits in municipalities of any size.

In the first place, Doc Mac, despite his skimpy beginnings, did come to enjoy a good professional income. Medical fees brought in $2,400 in 1913, and twice that amount in 1925. These earnings seem small in our day. In 1977, for instance, fifty years after the Doctor's death, the average American physician could count on $63,000 in annual professional receipts. But the 1920's were a different decade, and the dollars were different dollars.

Doc Mac *could* have earned more from his medicine than he did. But money did not mean that much to him. The only patients he enjoyed dunning were a few old skinflints who he thought deserved it. Furthermore, he always had a delicate conscience about demanding too much for his services. Finally, he sub-scribed completely to the noble medical tradition of charging the needy less – or nothing.

Some of this medical charity he practiced in the clinics of Corning Hospital. He practiced it much more in dealing with his own patients. The Doctor's account books contain many scrawled entries like the following: "McQuillen, $1.50"; "Pole, $1.50"; "Hungarian, $1.50"; "Italian, $1.50" (or even "Italian, $1.00"). These sums usually represented discounts from his "high" fee of $2.00 per office call.

In hardship cases, he would go farther. Frank Rice, for in-stance, had a sick wife and a light purse. The Doctor told him one day that he wished to bring another doctor into the case as a consultant. Frank replied that he didn't know how he could afford two doctors. "That's all right," said Doc Mac. "If you can pay the consulting physician, you can skip me."

Doctor McNamara always admired the Italian immigrants for their insistence on squaring medical accounts. Poor though they might be, they usually had a few dollars stashed away under the mattress for such emergencies.

True, the Lavisanos hesitated to pay him on one occasion, but that was because they were faced by a *double* emergency. When Mrs. Lavisano's new baby came, it was twins! "How much do I owe you, Doctor?" the father asked timidly. Doc saw the worried look in Lavisano's eyes. "Well," he answered, "I usually charge $25 per delivery, so for twins that would be $50. However, this was really one confinement case, so $25 will do."

Mrs. Docksie Jones was in even greater straits than the Rices and the Lavisanos. Docksie had been ill a long time, and when he died his widow was almost penniless. Knowing her situation, the Doctor gave her his bill, but with this written across the bottom of it, "Paid in full: T. A. McNamara."

Of course, Dr. McNamara did not allow charity to others to steal the bread from his own family. He was a great advocate of life insurance, and by 1904 he had laid away $17,000 in insurance – some with mutual benefit associations, but most with standard commercial insuring firms. He also invested rather large sums in government bonds, transportation bonds, industrial stock and other dependable securities. By 1921 the income from these securities amounted to $3,000 a year. No, his family would not be in need, then or thereafter, if he could help it.

He did have a scruple about earning too much from investments. Maybe it was his rural Yankee background showing through, but he was uncomfortable about getting money he had not somehow worked for. One year, for example, the Baltimore and Ohio Railroad Corporation, in which he held stock, unexpectedly declared a large cash dividend. This windfall really embarrassed him. Only when he had used it to buy something for one of his daughters and make a donation to charity did he recover from his chagrin.

Between 1901 and 1913, Doctor Mac did a little money-lending. He held twelve mortgages in all, running from $100 to $3,140. The largest loan was to a brother-in-law; and it is a fair guess that most of the others were also favors done to friends and patients. Business deals, yes; but benefactions as well.

Even his plunge into real estate during the same years had its beneficent aspect. McNamara the entrepreneur purchased two small plots on Corning's North Side around 1900. Upon this acreage he constructed about a dozen residences, inexpensively built and inexpensively priced. The smaller houses were on a short street he named "Evelyn Street" after his second daughter. They cost about $1,500 to erect. The larger homes were on Ellicott Street, and sold for about $3,000. Most, if not all, of the purchasers were families which first occupied the homes as renters. He sold at least two of the houses on "installment land contracts." By this arrangement, the rent paid by prospective buyers was applied to the eventual purchase price. It was a kindly sort of financing, in that it made a mortgage unnecessary. The Doctor was satisfied, in real estate as well as other investments, if he realized a six-percent return.

Today, Evelyn Street and its homes are no more – the victims, ultimately, of the Great June Flood of 1972. Some of the old McNamara houses around Ellicott Street are still in use. Although not architectural masterpieces, they are sound and comfortable.

From time to time, Corning people who wanted to break into a business enterprise would ask the Doctor's financial counsel. They knew about his successful ventures. They might have turned to him less confidently if they had been aware of his investments that failed.

His first business flop was a well-intentioned health institute, the "Highland Pines Sanitarium." Highland Pines had been opened in 1892 by another local physician, on a fine wooded knoll high on Corning's southern hill. The sanitarium was reorganized in 1902. Dr. John L. Miller of Corning was elected president of the new corporation; Dr. McNamara, vice-president. It stands to reason that both were stockholders. But "Highland Pines" shut down for good a year later. I do not know what the reason was, or what loss my father sustained.

Adventure No. 2 was more frankly a gamble, but apparently a very small one. In 1910, three Corning men decided to open an automobile factory in Corning. They bought out the Imperial Motor Car Company of Williamsport, Pa., along with its inventory of auto parts, valued at $25,000. Their first plan was to manufacture "Imperials" in Corning. Instead, after four years of indecision, they founded a new corporation, the Corning Motor Car Company. Their new aim was certainly bold: to produce a rival to Henry Ford's "tin-lizzie." According to the plans, their four-cylinder "Crystal City Cycle Car" would sell for only $375.

Doctor Mac was not one of the three original partners. Perhaps he invested no more than $25 in their scheme. But he did allow the mechanics to assemble the model car in his barn at 32 East First Street. They started working in May 1914 and finished in November. By that time, however, the total construction cost of the car had risen to $850. Of course, neither the Doctor nor any other sensible investor would have sunk one penny more into such a losing proposition. So the incorporators sadly auctioned off the one and only Crystal City Cycle Car, and dissolved their company. Henry Ford was no doubt relieved!

Adventure No. 3 was a copper-mining enterprise, the Royal Development. This cost the Doctor and his family a good deal more. The Royal Development was a corporation formed to open a copper mine in the Cascade Mountains of Washington State. A mining engineer named Naughten had located there a promising vein of ore, predominantly copper, and wanted to mine it. His brother, Father Francis J. Naughten, was pastor of St. Ann's Church, Hornell, N.Y. – the former parish of the McNamaras.

Francis Naughten himself was no gambler. Indeed, up to this point he had frowned on priests who invested in stocks and bonds. However, when his brother brought up the subject of mining for metal, the pastor began to think how pleasant it would be for the relatively poor local Catholics and the various diocesan institutions to invest in the project and reap a welcome benefit. So the Royal Development Corporation was organized, and St. Ann's rectory became its "stockbrokerage." Once founded, the Royal quickly caught the fancy of many Catholics in western New York.

Hearing of all this, Doctor Mac visited Father Naughten in 1918, and was charmed by the undertaking. Over the next few years he bought as many as 800 shares of Royal stock for himself and members of his family. Personally, he invested in some royalty certificates. The regular stock was protected, in that the purchase-money was straightway put into government bonds. But the "royalty certificates," based on the amount of ore mined, were strictly speculative.

During the next few years, the Doctor followed with zest progress reports about the mine. However, by the time of his last illness in 1927, the Royal operations had come to a virtual standstill. Interest on the deposited funds had proved inadequate for completing the tunnel, and the capital was, of course, protected from invasion. Furthermore, the ore was not so rich as had been anticipated. Only in 1940, ten years after the death of Father Naughten, did the company finally disband. Those who had put money into speculative certificates lost their gamble. Law suits nibbled away a good deal of the remaining assets. Nevertheless, the "little people" who possessed common stock, were still paid back eighty cents out of every dollar.

Adventures No. 4 and No. 5 swung back into automotives. Jesse G. Hawley, a Corning machinist, invented a timer designed for Ford automobiles. In 1921 he started turning these out in a barn across from Doc Mac's barn. When he organized a manufacturing company, Jesse offered the Doctor a chance to buy stock. His sales pitch was effective. Stock certificate #1, for three shares at a par value of $100, was made out to Thomas A. McNamara.

The timer may have been well conceived, but it didn't sell. Undaunted, Jesse went on to invent a shock-absorber. To produce these "snubbers," as he called them, he organized a new firm called the Hawdos Corporation. Again he invited the Doctor to buy in. Again the Doctor accepted, with undiminished enthusiasm. He purchased 81 shares, which represented about one-seventh of the total stock issued. In 1927 its value was estimated at $2,300. The new corporation, in turn, elected Doctor Mac vice-president. Hawdos was still making snubbers in 1927, but by the time of the market crash of 1929, two years after Vice-president McNamara's death, it had suspended production. Thus the Hawdos shares bequeathed by the Doctor to his children were ultimately of value only as souvenirs of "something ventured, something lost."

The sixth and last McNamara misadventure was the lots in Florida. Florida's great land-boom took place in the mid-1920's. Many northerners invested, sight unseen, in Florida real estate which was sometimes actually under water. However, when the Doctor decided to dabble, he was careful to seek knowledgeable counsel and deal with reputable realtors. He finally purchased several lots in the projected development called Hollywood Hills, located in the Miami area. Unfortunately, this subdivision was too remote from Miami for the land to increase in value with any rapidity. When the property was finally sold in the 1950's, the modest profit on paper was probably more than cancelled out by a quarter-century of real estate taxes dutifully paid.

How did these gambles of Doctor Mac square with his almost Yankee sensitivity about accepting money he had not earned? Maybe they didn't. Perhaps it was the Irishman coming through. (He always enjoyed being somewhat in debt. It gave him, he said, a hurdle to vault.) Obviously, however, none of his speculations involved a large sum. They were "fun" investments of expendable cash: a recreation for a man who had none of the commonplace hobbies.

Professional skill and business enterprise therefore won for the Doctor a public visibility and esteem in his community. Did it also win him "social" status?

In his era, being Irish and Catholic was usually a social disadvantage in any community predominantly Anglo-Saxon and Protestant. Three factors counterbalanced this disadvantage in the Doctor's case. First, since he was not a native of Corning, he could more easily maintain a happy detachment from the hereditary cliques. Second, although thoroughly Irish, he was not a "professional" Irishman, but rather an American proud of his Irish roots. Third, although thoroughly Catholic, he had learned from childhood how to be comfortable in respectable "ecumenical" company.

Christ Episcopal Church was just across the street from our house. Occasionally Doctor Mac would attend a service there when some "High Church" clergyman was preaching. But he was a punctilious member of his own parish, St. Mary's, and for years was both friend and physician of its clergy. Only once did he find himself at odds with a pastor, Father Colgan; and here the issue was not theological but medical.

Very Reverend Dean Peter Colgan, named rector of St. Mary's in 1862, was a native of Ireland. His flock gave him due credit as a builder of parish buildings and parish morals. The Corning business establishment recognized him as a canny business man. But he was also a clerical autocrat of the old Irish school.

Father Colgan had founded a small orphanage and entrusted it to the Sisters of Mercy, whom he brought to Corning in 1867 to staff his elementary school. (The school was run, by the way, on the "Poughkeepsie Plan," which incorporated it into the local public school system.) Some time in the mid-1890's, one of the little orphans was stricken by a high fever. Dr. Mac diagnosed the fever as most likely typhoid. Since the child attended the parish school, he advised the pastor to suspend classes as a preventive health measure.

For some reason, Father Colgan did not want to close the school. Since rumors of typhoid had quickly spread around Irish Hill, he addressed the subject from the pulpit on the following Sunday. To counter the rumors, he asserted that he had an expert to testify that the orphan's illness was *not* typhoid. He warned the congregation, therefore, to ignore anybody who was trying to raise a "false scare." He did not name the person who started the "rumor", nor did he name his own "expert." But it seems that his witness was none other than the assistant pastor, whose diagnostic qualifications were no greater than those of Colgan himself.

When Doctor McNamara heard the Dean's warning from the pulpit, he stormed in to confront him. "Father Colgan," he said, eyes ablaze, "You have publicly questioned my medical skill and judgment." In protest, he took his sons Adrian and Tom out of the "parish" school and transferred them to the Walnut Street public school.

The sick girl died. The pastor, caught in his own snare, gave her the quietest of funerals. Fortunately, there was no epidemic in St. Mary's School.

Dean Colgan had been irresponsible, yet he offered no apology; indeed, he no longer engaged the Doctor's professional services after that. The loss of one clerical patient did not particularly disturb Doctor Mac. Father Colgan was old at the time, and died not long afterward, on May 22, 1896. To succeed him at St. Mary's, the bishop of Buffalo named none other than Father James M. Bustin, Doctor Mac's old schoolmate and scholastic rival of the Niagara University days. It was a simple task to mend the broken fence. Adrian and Tom were brought back to St. Mary's School that fall and finished up there.

Fraternalism was one of the most popular movements in nineteenth century America, particularly in smaller communities. As a Catholic, Dr. McNamara could not join the Freemasons; but there were similar organizations that the Church did not rule out. Thus, he was a charter member of the Corning Elks. He also signed up with the Modern Woodmen of America, probably because of their insurance benefits. In 1897, a new Catholic fraternal society, the Knights of Columbus, established a council in Corning. Thomas A. McNamara welcomed the K. of C., became a charter knight, moved up through its four degrees of membership, and long served as its examining physician. In later years he delivered several lectures before the Corning Knights. It stands to reason, however, that a busy general practitioner like the Doctor would have had little time to participate in most of the recreational activities of any fraternal organization. Furthermore, he was too much an individualist to qualify as a typical "joiner."

The more a social movement could contribute to Corning's general welfare, the readier was Doc Mac to support it. He worked especially hard to bring Corning Hospital into existence and to promote its constant improvement.

Prolonged agitation to establish a community hospital in Corning finally resulted in the meeting of April 14, 1896, when a group of representative citizens gathered to plan a hospital drive for $25,000. The Doctor took part in that organizational meeting.

Corning Hospital opened on June 6, 1900. Thomas A. McNamara served as the first head of its medical and surgical staff. He took his turn working for the charity cases in its clinic. For many years thereafter he gave lectures on matters medical to its student nurses, ever seeking to remind them of the nobility of their calling. He also stressed this theme when, as mayor, he addressed the graduating class of the Nursing School's fifth commencement. "A nurse is a soldier," the Doctor told the graduating class, "and as such is likely to drop on the field of battle any moment." In those days, nurses were indeed subject to greater physical risk in the line of duty than they are at present. He spoke that day with two specific, but unnamed, cases in mind: "Two graduate nurses of Corning Hospital," he said, "have already achieved that honor."

When a questioner asks, however, about a person's social status he is usually less interested in the subject's parish, lodge, and charitable activities, than in his social acceptance by leaders of the community. What was the Doctor's social status in this sense?

Corning, although a small city, had the customary socialite groupings. The top stratum, as usual in upstate New York, was white, Anglo-Saxon, and Protestant. Dr. McNamara was not at all interested in sharing the pastimes of this stratum. Social climbing he held in amused disesteem.

Of course, some local Catholics went "lace curtain" and tried to mount the social ladder. One example is the couple whom we shall call Jack and Bessie. Jack, a bright and promising second-generation Irish-American, aspired to a political career. When he began to rise in State politics, he and Bessie thought it time to bid for recognition by Corning's "smart set." Having become pregnant, Bessie decided to entrust herself, not to Doctor Mac, their family physician, but to Doctor X, a non-Catholic who was patronized by the city's "carriage trade."

As Bessie's date of expectancy drew near, however, she began to have gestational problems. Since Doctor McNamara had the best reputation in the district for dealing with problem pregnancies, Doctor X called him in on the case as a consultant. Thanks to the consulting physician's advice, Doctor X was able to bring about a normal delivery.

Of course, Doctor Mac had many a quiet chuckle over the irony of the situation. However, he did not allow Jack's and Bessie's little gaffe to interfere with his long friendship with them.

While he had neither time nor inclination to socialize with the local elite, the Doctor could always spare time to chat with townsmen whom he admired as persons. He particularly enjoyed the company, for different reasons, of A. F. Smith, Charles Buckland, and Victor Cole. Alonso F. Smith was an undertaker and several other things. His talents lay largely hidden beneath a gruff exterior. Charles F. Buckland was a dentist, a wiry, mustached little man and a great story teller, who laughed so hard that he cried. Victor Cole, a druggist of dry wit, was stocky and bald, and wore a walrus mustache, wire spectacles, and black cambric oversleeves. His drugstore was long and narrow, and smelled of a thousand medicaments. Strictly an apothecary, he had no soda fountain in his establishment, and sold no sweetmeats but rock candy. Whenever the McNamara family could not locate the Doctor elsewhere, they could usually find him at Vic Cole's pharmacy.

Alonso, Charles and Vic were all Protestants. My father's staunchest Catholic friend after 1896 was his pastor, Father James Bustin. Father Bustin used to drop in at the Doctor's office with some regularity, for business or pleasure or both. The priest would take the oak armchair in the bay window, light up still another cigar, and launch into a lively discussion or argument with the physician. Maybe philosophy, maybe religion or cultural matters, maybe current events. Soon, the two would be shouting each other down. Mrs. McNamara, out in the kitchen, was always a little afraid that these uproars would end in mayhem. She could never quite appreciate that the two argufiers were simply renewing the debates of their college days.

In a small town, citizens live in a fishbowl. Visibility has merits in that it discourages flagrant public misbehavior. But it also fosters gossip, which can damage even the best reputations if not countered promptly and firmly.

In spite of his good reputation, Doctor McNamara became the object of a slanderous attack in 1899. An unidentified person spread the accusation that the Doctor had committed some mischief in the course of a professional call at the Wellington Hotel.

The only record of this slander is the letter which the Doctor himself sent to a local paper on March 11, 1899. Somebody, he wrote to the editor, had recently defamed him by asserting that he had misbehaved at a place where he had not been; and had there ministered to a certain person whom he declared he had never known. For over a year, he said, he had not called on, cared for, or treated *any* patient in the Wellington Hotel. Therefore, by means of this letter, he was announcing that he would pay a reward for the identification of his defamer.

Nobody responded in one way or another to this prompt rejoinder. Its very publication doubtless nipped the libel in the bud. Actually, the main result of the Doctor's rebuttal was probably to confirm Corningites in their high opinion of his integrity and his honesty. Eight years later, this physician who was already much in the public eye would be chosen to run for Corning's "supreme" political office, the mayoralty.

Picture Album

The Promised Land of Patrick McNamara. Steuben County, New York; its southern townships.

Thomas A. McNamara, Collegian
(1876 - 1879)

Clet Hall, Our Lady of Angels College and Seminary
(Niagara University), c. 1880

New York University, 1831
(R. Hinshelwood Engraving, 1836)

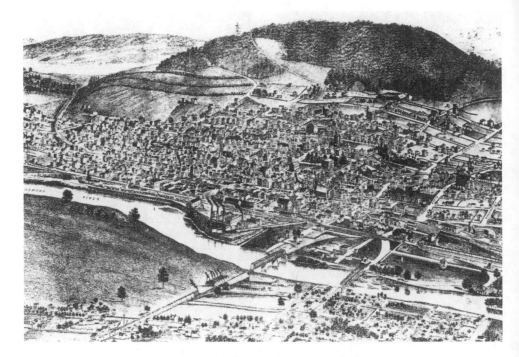

Village of Corning, 1882

Concert Block, Market and Pine Streets, Corning (c. 1850).
The Concert Hall, on the third floor, was totally removed in
the mid-twentieth century. Dr. Mac s first office was on the
second floor, alley-side: one "med" room, one bedroom.

Katherine Dwyer McNamara
(1863-1897)

32 East First Street, Corning (photo c. 1893):
home and office of Dr. T.A. McNamara (on porch).
Children, left to right: Frances McNamara, Thomas L.
McNamara, cousin Mary Alice McGannon,
and Adrian A. McNamara.

Patrick McNamara, Sr. and family, Hornellsville, N.Y., (c. 1890).
Seated: Patrick, Sr.; Frances (Mrs. William McCarthy);
Mary (Mrs. John L. Shannon).
Standing: Dr. Daniel; Dr. Patrick, Jr.; Dr. Alexander;
William; Dr. Thomas A.

Opening of Corning' s Denison Park, September 9, 1909.
George F. Showers, D.D.S., president, CBMA, (dais, r̲.)
delivers the deed to Mayor T.A. McNamara (dais, l̲.)

Back to Adrian: the hamlet' s Old Home Reunion, July 24, 1913:
"The chapel and schoolhouse upon the green mound."

Adrian, N.Y., 1913: the old home of railroader Patrick McNamara, Sr.; his surviving sons and daughters; and some of his grandchildren.

<u>Front row, left</u>: Dr. Thomas A McNamara, with Robert.

<u>Second row</u>: Dr. Thomas L. McNamara; William and Eleanor Pearsall McNamara, with Alexander; Frances McCarthy II; Madeline McNamara; Paul J. McNamara (son of Dr. Daniel); Dr. Alexander McNamara; Frances McNamara McCarthy (with William J. McCarthy): Helen Dwyer McNamara; Evelyn McNamara; Mary McNamara Shannon; Sarah McNamara Rannells; her father, Dr. Daniel McNamara; and her son, Edmund B. Rannells, Jr.

Old Dr. Mac and Young Dr. Mac operating in aseptic gear,
c. 1913. (Dr. Frank S. Swain, anesthetist.)

Ready for World War I, 1918.
Lieut. Thomas L. McNamara, M.D.; Helen Dwyer
McNamara; Robert McNamara; Dr. Thomas A.
McNamara, Chm., Exemption Board; Evelyn
McNamara; Madeline McNamara.

The Corning Exemption Board: Charles E. Bowers;
Thomas A. McNamara, M.D., Chm.; Harry E. Battin, M.D.,
and a departing draftee contingent, 1917-1918.

Thomas A. McNamara, M.D. c. 1925

CHAPTER FOUR

"Hizzoner" the Mayor

Doctor Mac, as we have already seen, was elected a Steuben County coroner in both 1884 and 1890. He ran, certainly in the second instance and probably in the first, as a Republican. Irish-Americans in general were almost as committed to the Democratic party as they were to the pope. But when the Doctor was thinking of entering the coroner's race, his father-in-law gave him a bit of practical advice. Thomas Dwyer was a Democrat and had held political offices in Corning as a loyal party member. Nevertheless, he counseled Dr. Mac that in a Republican county like Steuben and a Republican town like Corning, nobody could climb very high as a Democrat. So the Doctor enrolled in the Grand Old Party.

It was not that Thomas McNamara sought the coronership as a political office. He sought it as a medical office that happened to be elective. However, in 1907, the local Republican bigwigs waited on the Doctor to invite him to run that fall for a truly political post, the Corning mayoralty.

That they should have invited a medico to be a candidate was not unusual. Corning's first mayor and two of his successors had been medical doctors. That they should have asked a Catholic to

run was more surprising. In a town where Protestants constitut-
ed the cultural majority, this unsought Republican invitation said
much about the Doctor's local prestige.

Completely surprised by the proposal, the Doctor at first
rejected it. The duties of mayor, he told the delegation, would
consume too much of the time that he owed to his busy medical
practice. "Not at all!" rejoined the committee. Corning's mayor,
they said, as a part-time official, had only one weekly meeting to
attend, and there would be few other demands. They pressed,
they cajoled, and finally they conquered. Nevertheless, the Doctor
said that if he consented to be on the ballot, it was reluctantly.

Election day fell on November 5, 1907. Doctor Mac won
handily over Frederick Ellison, his Democratic opponent. He
was no doubt flattered by the outcome. Any novice candidate
would have been.

But the very day after his victory at the polls, the mayor-elect
began to experience just the sort of troubles he had feared.
Though not yet inaugurated, he was besieged by citizens clam-
oring for future favors. Inexperienced as he was in political
shenanigans, he saw that he had accepted too readily the party
leaders' assurances that the mayor's office was a sinecure. When
he then began to draw up a list of city appointments, he received
another lesson in practical politics. His intention was to name
the men *he* believed to be the best qualified. The party, it turned
out, intended him to name the men *they* wanted.

On January 5, 1908, His Honor, Mayor Thomas A. McNamara,
had his first meeting with the Common Council. That session
almost became a donnybrook.

The Mayor had already announced his candidates for
appointive offices, subject, of course, to Council confirmation.
The aldermen chose to table three of these nominations. The
Doctor was especially upset when they rejected, by a "pocket
veto," Francis E. Wood, his Republican nominee for city attorney. That meant that the current city attorney, Francis Williams,
would continue in office, although he was a Democrat. The
Mayor finally accepted defeat; but he made it quite clear that it

was not he who was presenting Mr. Williams for the office.

Then the new mayor blew his top.

"When I was nominated for the office of mayor," he told the aldermen, "it was against my will. I get $16 a month, you get $4, and I would gladly change places." Ever since election day, he said, he had been losing just too much of his valuable professional time. In spite of this initial flare-up, Dr. McNamara made the best of a bad bargain. He had been given a mandate, and he was determined to live up to his oath of office. During the two years of his term he did not miss a meeting of the Common Council. He was alert to his civic responsibilities; he spoke out only when he had done his homework; and in his messages and decisions he showed himself truly interested in community progress and political reform.

Early in 1908, Mayor McNamara delivered his first annual "state of the city" address to the aldermen and a small group of spectators. He began by praising the civic accomplishments of Corning, its government departments, its school systems. He welcomed the foundation of two new independent educational institutions, the Corning Commercial School and the very promising Bostelmann Conservatory of Music.

In the near future, he continued, the city would have to undertake a number of public improvements. *What* improvements he did not then specify; but he stated that the best way to finance them would be by issuing city bonds. A bond issue would, of course, necessitate an increase in property assessments. He believed, however, that the citizens would go along with the increase if it were levied fairly.

Next, he commended the Corning police force on its efficiency. He did recommend, though, that the city engage another policeman, one who was himself Italian or was able to communicate with the Italian-speaking. "This plan," he promised, "will not only strengthen the Police Department by closer touch with the industrious foreign element seeking work and homes in our city, but would stimulate its rapid assimilation."

Here was a calm analysis of the perceived achievements and

needs of his small municipality. The *Evening Leader* praised it as "able and sensible." "It is," the editor wrote, "a frank and straightforward sort of document that breathes the right spirit." The *Leader* was especially pleased by the suggestion that an Italian-speaking officer be added to the police force.

During the twenty-four months he was in office, this medical mayor was naturally on guard against anything that might endanger public health and safety. Thus, on July 30, 1908, a tragic accident occurred at the Erie Railroad grade crossing on lower East First Street. A passenger train, coming around the curve, struck a Standard Oil delivery wagon, seriously injuring a man and killing a young woman. The aldermen had discussed this hazardous crossing a month before but had taken no action. On August 3, the Mayor communicated his concern about the problem and proposed several interim safety precautions. It seems that these safety measures were acted upon. (Four years later the city achieved a permanent solution. A bridge was constructed to carry the trains at this point, and a "subway" was dug to carry the street underneath the bridge.)

All the more intent, after his collision with local politicos, to reform Corning's government, the Doctor began to study alternate types of city management that might be more efficient and less open to political manipulation. After a good deal of private research, he delivered to the aldermen, on December 14, 1908, a reformist address that startled them.

The city of Corning, according to its original 1890 charter, was governed by a mayor and an aldermanic council. This charter had been revised twice, but still labored under some odd inconsistencies. The mayor might be called "His Honor"; he might, said the Doctor, have the veto power that distinguished a "strong" mayor from a ceremonial mayor. But although he could vote on three of the city boards, he still had no vote on the important boards of police and public works.

When a boy grows tall, Mayor McNamara continued, his suit of clothes no longer fits him. Corning had now outgrown its original suit, and needed a new one – that is, a new charter.

He proposed that the best type of city government would be one that left no opening for partisan politics and patronage. What format did he judge best? A commission form of government – Texas type – would come closest to filling the bill.

A city commission, he explained, comprises three-to-five members. All the members are elected directly by the citizens, and their tenure of office depends on their own efficiency and good behavior. This structure reduces political control and patronage. He granted that commission government is not perfect, but he believed its merits outweigh its shortcomings. Several cities in Texas, he said, had tried it and found it effective: Galveston, Dallas, Fort Worth and Houston. The commission government at Haverhill, Massachusetts, was also working well; and several other municipalities in the same state were considering the adoption of the plan.

The Mayor's proposal struck the Common Council like a bolt from the blue, although, when the time came for comments, nobody commented. Of course, the plan did involve a "radical departure," as the *Corning Daily Journal* observed the following day.

Having concluded his formal presentation, Dr. McNamara added, off-the-cuff, "These are my views on the question. You can accept them or not, just as you like... Under the present charter, the aldermen do not amount to anything."

The *Daily Journal* properly praised Mayor McNamara for the "careful preparation" that his address evidenced. The *Evening Leader* said the recommendation deserved "serious discussion." There is no evidence, however, that the Common Council or anybody else in town followed the *Leader*'s advice. The aldermen would probably have been wary about such a "radical departure."

"Hizzoner" nevertheless soon set about writing his second "state of the city" message, which he delivered in February 1909. Once again, he recommended that the city adopt a commission form of government. Aware by now that his suggestion had not been warmly welcomed, he simply mentioned it and passed on calmly to other matters. At least he had tried. (Corning shifted to a city manager – ceremonial mayor structure on July 1, 1998.)

He was happy to report that the property reassessment he had favored in 1908 had been carried out. Turning then to the improvements needed, he said that a second vehicular bridge over the river deserved a high priority. It had often been discussed but never decided on. Yet, he said, "like Banquo's ghost, the matter of another bridge across the Chemung River will not down." On November 28, 1908, he told his audience, the Board of Public Works had taken a count of the users of the Bridge Street bridge. Even though the factories were not operating that day, 5,548 persons had crossed the river on foot, 2,250 by trolley, and 1,400 in wagons. This, he maintained, was excessive use, and could only imperil the bridge's structure. (The city did not react positively to his warning. Corning would wait twelve years more to get that second bridge. There were, however, some extenuating reasons for the delay.)

Another hazard to life and health, the Mayor continued, was the mode of garbage disposal. This issue had particularly engaged him as a medical man since spring 1908, when the number of local cases of typhoid fever had been unusually high. The Board of Health had promptly tested the local water supply and milk supply and had found them innocent of infection; but the Board had nonetheless continued its investigation. Now the Doctor was pleased to announce that a special joint committee of the City Council and the Board of Health was examining a model garbage-disposal unit located at Wilkes Barre, Pennsylvania. (This study would produce positive results. In June 1909, the Common Council, on the basis of the joint committee's report, voted for the construction of a new incinerating plant in Corning.)

Continuing his remarks on the "state of the city," the Mayor recalled that Steuben County had lately decided to establish in Corning a county bacteriological laboratory. In the name of the city, he pledged that the local government would assist this important health project in every way possible.

In conclusion, Mayor McNamara spoke enthusiastically about the forthcoming completion of Corning's first real park. He had followed its development with deep interest. "We have," he declared, "a great future in the Crystal City!" For him the new park was a special symbol of that future.

Corning's Denison Park would indeed be a joy to all Corningites. The project was backed by the Corning Business Men's Association, the predecessor of the Corning Chamber of Commerce. In 1906, the CBMA bought a plot of thirty-one riverside acres on the lower south side of town. The property cost $8,400. Its landscaping and outfitting would cost about twice that price.

To raise funds, the CBMA staged a "Society Circus" in August, 1908. The performers were local amateurs, but the impresario and ringleader was an old circus professional, John Comosh. Corning-born Comosh was now a coal dealer and a member of the Business Men's Association. But in the 1870's and 1880's, this Portuguese-American had been a circus acrobat. Traveling with various American circuses under the name of John Worland, he had thrilled thousands with his unique triple somersault over a lineup of elephants and horses.

Although the Society Circus was a success, its receipts went only part way toward paying off the bill of $24,000. Fortunately, the Association now got the ear of Charles L. Denison, a former Corningite who had made himself a pretty penny in the national business world. Denison was willing to strike a bargain with the CBMA. If the park were named after his late father, Charles G. Denison, he would pay off the rest of the $15,000 debt. So Denison Park it became.

By late summer 1909, all that remained was for the Association to deed over the new facility to the city. The ceremonial transfer was set for Labor Day, September 9, 1909. On that holiday, citizens from all over "metropolitan Corning" streamed parkward on foot, in carriages, or in trolleys.

Climax of the dedication was the presentation of the deed. George F. Showers, D.D.S., president of the CBMA, was the presenter. Accepting for the city was Mayor McNamara. There were speeches, of course, and the Mayor's was much too long. But he did testify to the community's delight with this new public commons. "Yes, my friends," he said, "this is a day of jubilation for the people of Corning!"

The opening of Denison Park took place four months before Dr. McNamara's mayoral term expired. It can be considered, however, as the real climax of his mayoralty. He must have been gratified to have his frustrating but dutiful administration wind down so amiably.

The local Republican leaders most likely did not consider asking the Doctor to run for a second term. For them he was doubtless too individualistic, and even rather "dangerous." Had they asked him, he certainly would have declined. In the fall of 1909 the Democrats again put forward Frederick Ellison. This time Ellison won, falling heir to the title "Hizzoner" and the vast salary that went with that distinction.

If Doc Mac was to avoid henceforth the turmoil of elective office he was always ready to serve in appointive positions. When the federal government called upon him during World War I to "do his bit," on the home front, he responded generously.

World War I began in 1914 as a European struggle. On April 6, 1917 the United States, shocked by Germany's indiscriminate submarine warfare, decide to cast its lot with the European Allies.

Born five years before the outbreak of the Civil War, Thomas A. McNamara doubtless remembered the excitement of 1861-1865, and as a boy must have marched the short, dusty streets of Adrian to its martial tunes. He always considered America the noblest of nations – ever improvable, of course, but ever to be loved and defended. Sixty-one when we entered the World War, he was beyond the age for enlisting or drafting. But he was ready to do whatever else he could to "make the world safe for democracy."

For his own family, he set the pattern of patriotism. He encouraged young Dr. Tom to enlist in the Army Medical Corps. (Tom was commissioned first lieutenant on July 8, 1918.) He took it for granted that his wife and daughters would be active in the local Red Cross. For myself, aged six, he provided (or at least smiled at) a natty khaki soldier's uniform, puttees, haversack, "campaign ribbons" and all. At the city level, he became one of the campaigners for the "Liberty Loans" that were launched to finance war operations.

Up to World War I, with the exception of the Civil War, our American warriors had been volunteers. The U. S. Army of World War I was basically an army of draftees. As early as May 18, 1917, Washington legislated a plan of selective conscription. According to this plan, each section of the nation was expected to provide its quota of able-bodied men aged 21-30.

The War Department designated the eastern half of New York's Steuben County as the county's "Division No. 1" for conscription purposes. On June 23, Dr. Mac was informed by the Assistant Secretary of War that he had been appointed to the processing board of this division. Also appointed were Corningites Dr. Harry E. Battin and Mr. Charles E. Bowers. This committee of three was given office space in Corning's county courthouse. Dr. McNamara was at once designated chairman of the board, and he continued in the chair as long as the board functioned.

Today, a board of this sort would usually be called a "draft board." In 1917-1919 it was commonly called the "Exemption Board." While one of its functions was indeed to decide which of the draftees deserved exemption from service, its main duty was to provide the armed forces with able-bodied soldiers.

Initial drawing of the draft numbers took place in Washington on July 20, 1917. On July 31, the Corning Exemption Board received orders to supply 133 prospective servicemen. The Board at once summoned 229 local registrants for examination. On September 17, 1917, the first seven men who qualified set out for training camp. Corning honored these sheepish but willing pioneers with a public banquet. After the meal they were marched over to the Erie Railroad station to the music of a cornet band, with the Corning Home Guard Company to set the pace. A crowd of enthusiastic citizens was there to see them off (and probably also to give food, cigarettes and other little gifts to the rest of the men crowding the "troop train").

Later contingents of prospective doughboys may not have been treated to a banquet, but all departing groups were given a formal "Good-bye, good luck and God bless you!" Over the next year these departure ceremonies took place about once a month, and an address by Doctor Mac was pretty much a part of the rite. Later delegations were much larger than the first. They entrained for various camps in the east: Camp Devens, Camp Dix, Camp Upton, Fort Jackson, Fort Slocum. By the time the War Department called a halt to conscription, Corning alone had sent off 1,228 of its youth with cheers and tears.

Why had the federal government named two physicians to the Corning Exemption Board? Most likely because the conscripted had to pass a strict physical examination. But the trio of the Corning board also had a good many administrative duties.

Chairman McNamara worked overtime on his assignment. It robbed him of more hours than the mayoralty had, but he found this federal task far more congenial. To the hundreds of young men who (in the words of the contemporary song) "didn't know much what this war's about," he was not a bureaucrat but a father image. As the *Evening Leader* would recall a decade later, "He always found time to take a personal interest in the men who came before him for examination, and each contingent that left the city was given words of valuable advice. "

World War I came to a welcome halt when the armistice was signed on November 11, 1918. During the five weeks prior to Armistice Day, Doctor Mac had been overburdened by emergency medical duties. The great international epidemic of Spanish influenza hit Corning early in October. According to the report of the local Board of Health, 3,500 Corningites had been stricken by the end of that month, and 72 had died.

Early in March 1919, the War Department sent word to all draft boards that on March 31 they would be dissolved and their members honorably retired from duty. Citations were sent on that date to the members of each board, signed by Provost Marshal General Enoch H. Crowder and countersigned by Governor Alfred E. Smith. Then on April 6, General Crowder, who had supervised the national conscription organization, sent to the same ex-members another form letter of praise. "You have performed a stupendous task," he wrote. "You have performed it loyally, unselfishly and well... you have laid the ground work for a new ideal of democracy..." Form letters or not, these communications must have gratified the conscientious McNamara, Battin and Bowers.

Five years later the trio received yet another letter from Washington. The U. S. Adjutant General asked the recipients whether they thought that the men who had served on the American exemption boards might enjoy receiving the U. S. Victory Medal as a token of recognition.

To this odd query, the three Corning addressees sent a joint reply, probably composed by Doctor Mac. Yes, they believed the former board members would appreciate the Victory Medal. It would remind them of a pleasant duty done; it would inspire their descendants; and it would be a concrete symbol of the nation's gratitude for patriotic services rendered. Of course, they added, the task had brought its own reward, that of "being able to add our mite to the great cause." But it was clear that the three Corning men themselves would have been quite pleased to receive the decoration.

Now, I am sure I would remember if the government had sent my dad a Victory Medal. He would certainly have displayed it and taken precautions that his descendants preserve it as an "inspiration." Perhaps the Adjutant General found in the end he didn't have enough medals to go around.

Thomas A. McNamara had certainly shown unquestioning loyalty to his community and to his national government before Armistice Day. After the war, however, he dissented sharply from, and even on occasion made light of, one set of American laws – those prohibiting alcoholic beverages.

The 18th Amendment to the federal Constitution, all too hastily voted in by the majority, was declared effective from January 16, 1920. (Even before the constitutional amendment was adopted, many localities had zealously outlawed the sale of alcohol by "local option." Thus, Corningites had voted as early as April 1918 against the local issuance of liquor licenses.)

Doc Mac seldom drank hard liquor. He had seen what it could do to his patients and to some of his kin. But he did enjoy a glass of beer on a hot summer's day or a glass of wine on a holiday. Just before the government lowered the boom, the Doctor, like many other Corningites, bought a few cases of wine at nearby Hammondsport – "Golden Age" brand, I believe. Doled out sparingly on major family feasts, this precious "reserve" lasted several years.

The 18th Amendment was certainly stringent. While it implied that some alcoholic liquids could be made and circulated for other than "beverage" purposes, it sternly forbade the importation, manufacture, transportation and sale of "intoxicating" liquors. Even more puritanical was the enabling law known as the "Volstead Act," which took effect on January 17, 1920. This law defined as "intoxicating" any liquor containing more than one-half of one percent of alcohol. And even in the area of permissible beverages (for medicinal or sacramental use), the legislators and enforcers tended to be persnickety.

For example, in July 1921, a bill was presented to Congress that would have restricted physicians from prescribing beer medicinally. When this issue was raised, the Corning *Leader* asked the local medicos what they thought of beer as a medicine. Some doctors refused to comment (public favor for prohibition may have made them cautious). A dozen did state their views. Most of them had no objection to the bill, since they believed beer to have no curative value. But three doctors – all Catholics, by the way – opposed the legislation because it would tie the hands of the physician. They were Dr. John F. Dwyer and the two McNamaras.

Thomas A. McNamara gave the strongest and most thorough reply, addressing not only the proposed legislation but the whole issue of prohibition.

Throughout his thirty-nine years of practice, he said, he had found beer invaluable in the treatment of cholera infantum, cholera morbus, and extreme hemorrhage. His view had been long since confirmed by an article by Dr. Abraham Jacobi in *The Lancet*, Britain's top medical journal.

Today, he went on, some over-zealous advocates of prohibition were pushing the pendulum too far. The pharmacopoeia had always included alcohol, although many physicians, under the pressures of prohibition, were now shutting their eyes to its benefits. He himself was entirely in agreement with Dr. Jacoby [*sic*], whom he called one of the greatest pathologists of the age. Several years before the 18th Amendment was voted in, Jacobi had denounced medically "the movement of extreme prohibition."* "We are not dealing here," Doctor Mac insisted, "with a moral issue."

However noble its aim to conquer drunkenness and its social side-effects, federal prohibition did not succeed and could not have succeeded. Most Catholics shared with Doctor McNamara the view that the immorality of alcohol lay not in its use but its abuse. Most Americans, whatever their ethical persuasions, finally reached the same practical conclusion. The liquor industry had not vanished but had gone underground, and clandestine bars called "speakeasies" replaced the notorious public saloon. Of course, the liquor laws never prohibited the home manufacture of alcoholic drinks, so many householders began to ferment their own unprofessional wine and brew their own unprofessional beer.

Doctor Mac himself did a little "home-brewing." He also did a little "speakeasying," evidently without a twinge of conscience.

One summer, he decided to become a brewer. He put a large crock in the cool cellar, filled it with water, stirred in the grain, yeast and other ingredients, and looked forward eagerly to a batch of refreshing Pilsener. Fermentation soon set in, but then something went awry. Either the process malfunctioned, or fruit flies invaded the vat, or he himself just got tired of waiting. Anyhow, having decided to call it quits, he poured out the mash on the back lot. If the experiment had brought him no pleasure, it sent the local birds into raptures. The robins and sparrows soon

---

*Abraham Jacobi, M.D. (1830 – 1919), a native of Germany, established himself in New York City in 1853 as a practitioner and professor of pediatrics. In his practice he had found alcohol truly medicinal in diphtheria and other mixed infections.

discovered the fermented grain, gorged themselves on it, and flopped away "drunk as owls."

The Doctor also visited at least one local speakeasy. This was the establishment run by Cassius G. Andrew, a stocky, toupéed publican who for years had operated a respectable pub at 12 West Market Street. After the ban on liquor, Cass continued to preside at the old stand, serving pop and "near-beer" across the old-fashioned hardwood bar. However, trusted clients and friends could purchase stronger stuff from *under* the bar.

One day, Doc discovered a booklet of recipes for mixed drinks. Most of them he had never heard of, and they piqued his "scientific" curiosity. So he began to visit Andrew's establishment regularly for a while. Each day he would order a different drink from the booklet, drink it analytically, and check it off the list. When he had crossed off the last of the recipes, he stopped these "laboratory tests."

Too bad Thomas McNamara did not survive until December 5, 1933, when the 21st Amendment officially canceled the 18th. Its quick ratification showed that America had come to understand what the Doctor had maintained all along – that alcohol in itself is neither moral nor immoral.

By December 1933, the mortal remains of "Hizzoner" Ex-Mayor McNamara had been at rest for six years in St. Mary's Cemetery. After his death, the local branch of the American Legion located beside his granite marker one of the small bronze flagstaffs it places at veterans' graves. Every Memorial Day the Legion inserts a small new American flag in each of these holders. The former mayor had never worn a military uniform, of course, but he had readied many a young man to serve in the uniformed forces. Apart from that one dissent from American law – the legislation on prohibition – Doc Mac was truly loyal to his native land. And when called upon to serve his city as its mayor and his nation and state as chairman of a wartime draft board, he had discharged the duties wisely and well.

— CHAPTER FIVE —

"A Home-loving Man"

The old "G.P.", as a "specialist in everything medical," was on call around the clock. His wife and children had to adjust to this irregularity of presence. Anything like a fixed "children's hour" was simply out of the question.

Dr. McNamara partly compensated for his absences by having the office at home. Thus, he kept in pretty close contact with the family even on his most irregular days. He also had a special means of signaling his arrival to the children and summoning them to board or bed. Stepping outdoors, he would whistle a mighty "whee-ah-*whee*" through his fingers. The brood would race home on the double, or else...

Apart from the unpredictable professional absences, the Doctor was a provident and attentive parent. Provident. He made enough money to take care of all essentials and even some frills. He never squandered. Indeed, in his purchases he adhered to the firm, if unstated principle, "Second-grade is just as good."

The McNamara home was roomy and pleasant. If the front yard was shallow, the back lot was deep. When the Doctor first purchased this property, the backyard had a wooden privy at a discreet distance, and was hemmed in by a tall, slivery plank

fence. Around 1900, Doctor Mac updated the residential plumb-
ing, erected a small alley-side barn to shelter horse and carriages, and replaced the fence with privet hedging. Then he gradually planted around the lawn a number of old-fashioned peren-
nials: lilacs, pink hydrangea trees, golden glow, iris, peonies,
lilies-of-the-valley, and rambler roses. Violets planted themselves. There were also a couple of old-fashioned rose bushes.
His favorite of these was the moss rose. Its tiny pink buds broke
forth from furry, sticky calyxes that had a geranium-sweet scent
of their own. During the long moss-rose season, Doc would cut
off a new bud each day to wear in his lapel. (He loved sweet
odors, and even at times used a bit of inexpensive "perfumery."
This may have been in part to offset the reek of ether that his
clothing absorbed during hospital visits.) There were also two
pear trees on the lot. The Bartlett produced fine fruit dripping
with juice. It was, in all, a congenial yard for kids to play in. The
grownups used it more often for drying clothes and beating rugs.
But they, too, enjoyed its garden-swing, its green quiet in late
afternoon, and the fireflies that winked in the dusk.

Of course, the boys of the family had the duty of sweeping
industrial and railroad soot off the porch, mowing the lawn, rak-
ing and burning the leaves, removing winter snow and ice from
the walks, and shoveling fuel into and ashes out of the coal fur-
nace. Frank Weldon was hired to do the heavier work, like lay-
ing bricks and building arbors. Frank was an ageless handy man,
sturdy, strong, and skillful. His black eyes were hooded, and he
had a swarthy, lined face. I learned only many years later that he
was of American Indian stock. Thus, when my father, in 1915,
added a lean-to sleeping porch to the upper back of the house, it
was Frank who laid the brick foundations for the supporting pil-
lars. (This was a very inexpensive sleeping porch, by the way,
not winterized; but it was heavenly for summer sleeping – quiet,
airy, and especially cozy when the rain pattered over its asphalt
roof and tinkled down its gutter.)

How shall I describe the interior of Doctor Mac's castle?
(Here details are important. Only they can help reveal what

made 32 East First Street especially "homey.")

It had an entrance hall, a front and back parlor on the left (matching the office and dining room on the right); a big kitchen; and, on the second floor, five bedrooms. Among the more stable fixtures were the black-walnut banister (fine for sliding down); the tall pier glass in the front parlor (convenient for primping); the chandeliers (one for electricity and gas, one with four Aurene lampshades, and one crafted in Tiffany glass). By the front door there was an umbrella stand of glazed purple stoneware, and in the back parlor, a resonant upright piano made by Wegman of Auburn, New York. Chairs and couches represented every period from Civil War Victorian to 1920's overstuffed. Included were a "mission style" armchair, two squeaky wicker armchairs, and two adjustable "Morris" chairs. Furnishings in the bedrooms were equally undistinguished: high-backed wooden beds and oaken dressers in three of the rooms, and brass beds and fussier furniture in the girls' bedrooms. But what the fittings lacked in distinction, they made up for in convenience, except for a few stubborn dresser drawers.

You could find items of distinction only in the dining room cupboards. Table linens hand-embroidered by the family. Dessert plates nicely hand-painted by Aunt Maggie McGannon. And, of course, in the "Crystal City," the inevitable fine glassware from one of the several local factories. Few homes in Corning were without some deep-cut crystal dishes, or samples of the iridescent Aurene glass designed by Frederick Carder of the local Steuben Glass Works. (If Corningites could not afford "firsts" in local glassware, they could always purchase "seconds," whose slight flaws escaped all but the expert eye.)

From time to time, current fashion demanded that the Macs acquire some popular luxuries. In 1914, the luxury was a record-player. A decade later, it was a radio.

In making both purchases, Doc again followed his axiom "Second-grade is just as good." The leading record player in 1914 was the Victor Company's "Victrola." Runner-up was the Columbia Company's rival the "Grafonola." Both were wound up by a crank, of course, and both could play any make of disk records. The Doctor chose the Grafonola.

We got a lot of service from our "talking machine." The girls bought or borrowed the latest dance hits – two-steps, fox trots, waltzes. (I recall especially "Ragging the Scale", "Too Much Mustard," "Auf Wiedersehen," and the "Princess Pat" waltzes.) Doctor Mac preferred the sweet songs of John McCormack or Sir Harry Lauder. He also enjoyed comic ditties like "Get Out and Get Under" and "Go Right Down Where You Belong." Comic ethnic records – "Cohen on the Telephone" for example – were still in favor. The whole family was interested in anything by the Peerless Quartet, a pioneer "barbershop" group. Al Campbell, one of the earliest Peerless members, was a Corning boy and a good friend of the McNamaras.

The Doctor bought our first radio in early 1924. At that time *the* deluxe apparatus was a "super-heterodyne", equipped with six "tubes." Papa chose a *five*-tube receiver made by Lafayette and dubbed a "neutrodyne". A large wet battery furnished the power. The sounds that came out of its horn-shaped hard-rubber loudspeaker were seldom certain. Weak signals and heavy static were inevitable when one lived in a valley. But we did hear much of the exciting Democratic presidential convention of 1924 with its memorable refrain: "Alabama: 24 votes for Underwood."

Housekeeping, cooking, canning, sewing and mothering were, of course, the undisputed departments of the two gentle-women who successively bore the name "Mrs. Thomas A. McNamara." Fortunately, the Doctor was able to afford helpers for the lady of the house, both for daywork and as live-in assistants.

Dressmaker Hulda Frisk, for example, was hired each year for several days at a time, to create (or more often re-create and repair) the family's clothing. Hulda, prim and exact at the sewing machine, spoke with a distinct Swedish accent.

From the 1890's to the 1920's, the Mrs. McNamaras also had helpers in residence much of the time. These were girls in their late teens. The Doctor gave them room and board and a salary of $8.00 per week the first year, $10.00 per week the second year.

Nice young women, they became practically members of the family. They picked up housekeeping arts and skills, and usually found a husband after a year or so.

Mary Boyle, for instance, was on the "staff" in the 1890's, and did much of the cooking. Before long, she struck up an acquaintance with young Tom Tunney, a cheery native of the County Mayo, who daily delivered the groceries at McNamara's kitchen door. In 1900 Tom and Mary were joined in marriage at St. Mary's Church. Tom later became one of the city's leading food merchants.

Katherine Marx lived with the Macs in 1912-1913. Lonesome for her native Germany, she found a new father and family at 32 East First Street. Before long, she met and married a beau of German background. Bertha Kerchinski, in residence 1914-1916, was a sweet girl from the coal-mining district of northern Pennsylvania. She was eventually wed to a railroad mechanic, Charles Sullivan. Martha Witucki, another gentle Polish-American girl, joined us in the early 1920's. All four of these helpers were Catholics. Pretty Evelyn Danielson, who came to us around 1919, was presumably Lutheran. I think her family lived in the Scandinavian neighborhood on Corning's North Side.

If Doctor Mac economized on furniture and appliances, he was very generous with the family's food budget. Leftovers were used, of course, and imaginatively. But the meats – roasts, beef-tongue, chops, fowl – were always choice and varied. The Lady of the House was traditionally a stellar baker. Apple and lemon meringue were the favorite pies; among the cakes, chocolate, marble, sponge, and (on birthdays) angel food, enjoyed special popularity. McNamara fried cakes, molasses, and sugar cookies deserved five stars. The hot Johnny-cake, made with buttermilk, was just right. But the most notable breadstuff was a hearty whole wheat bread. Dairy farmer Florence Rapalee of Himrod, New York, provided the spread for it. At stated intervals she sent down a ten-pound pail of butter via the New York Central Railroad.

Turkeys are commonplace today. In the Doctor's time they

appeared on his table only at Thanksgiving and Christmas. Either he or Young Doctor Tom did the carving, utilizing their surgical expertise. During these great feasts (at least before Prohibition made it impossible) there was always a bottle of New York State champagne, served in hollow-stemmed glasses of deep-cut Corning crystal.

For Doc Mac, the supreme refresher was ice cream. Often when he returned from his calls on a summer evening he would bring home a quart or two of ice cream, usually vanilla. He at once ate two helpings of it and expected everybody else, family and guests, to do the same.

Have I lingered too gluttonously on these tasty memories? At least they show that the head of the McNamaras did not starve his own flesh and blood.

How was the Doctor as husband and parent in other respects? Both attentive and affectionate. Kate Dwyer McNamara presented her Tom with seven children. Eleanor (1891) and Veronica Grace (1894) died as infants. The five who reached maturity were: Adrian Alexander, the first-born (1886); Thomas Leo (1888); Frances (1890); Evelyn Marie (1892); and Madeline (1896).

Adrian developed into a handsome, talented young fellow, full of his father's intense energy. Tom was gifted, too; although as the second son, more self-effacing. I never remember hearing Frances's traits discussed. She was blonde and truly beautiful, but perhaps constitutionally frail. Evelyn had chestnut hair, a sweet face, and humorous blue eyes. She resembled her mother in temperament and practicality. Madeline's hair was darker and her features were less regular. Left motherless in the first year of her life, she was always inclined to underestimate her own abilities. By nature she was outgoing and had a gift for friendship.

I was the only child of my father's second wife, Nell. Although his first family was pretty much grown up by the time I arrived, I have always felt that I belonged more to their generation (call it the "ragtime-Victor Herbert generation") than to the "Charleston generation" of my own contemporaries.

Both of Doc Mac's wives agreed with him on policies of parenting. Children should be raised with watchful care, spiritually, physically and socially. That was how he and his wives had been trained, and they could think of no better way.

The Doctor's family were not much given to sharing prayer. His absences would probably have discouraged formal grace at meals and the family rosary. But prayerful they were; and about the house there were crucifixes, religious statues and pictures, a Christmas crib, and a blessing from Pope Pius X – all reminders of the other world. (The favorite statue was a handsome, though handless, bisque image of the Blessed Virgin Mary. According to family tradition, Mary had even saved the house from burning. One night [before I was born] an oil lamp broke on the table where the image stood, and the cloth runner on the table caught fire. But the fire burnt only up to the base of the statue, and then sputtered out.)

Of course, the Macs sent their children to St. Mary's School, three blocks up Irish Hill. Had there been a Catholic high school in Corning, they would probably have gone there, too. On the other hand, the public high school, Corning Free Academy, was a good one, and it provided Catholic children with a wider acquaintance among their non-Catholic peers.

Youngsters who have a physician for a father can count on good medical care. Medical dads can sometimes seem overly cautious, however. For instance, many of the boys in our neighborhood owned air rifles. Not the Mac boys. Their father had seen far too many kids seriously injured, even blinded, by BB shot.

One social caution of the McNamara parents was their discretion of speech in the presence of the children. I am not speaking of profanity or indecent speech. The McNamaras and Dwyers were all sticklers in this matter, and would certainly have soaped out any young mouth that uttered offensive language. (Perhaps it was my father's sensitivity to sexual language that deterred him from even discussing with me the "facts of life." This omission has always puzzled me. As a scientist and a religious man he could have been an ideal tutor.) No, by discretion of speech, I mean rather a caution about discussing shocking, violent subjects. Only once did my parents forget their rule in my regard. That was the case of the Harry Smith murder.

In 1919, one Harry Smith, a resident of the Corning area, was brutally slain. Suspicion quickly fell upon a Hornby man named Jady Kelly. Kelly's trial took place in the county courthouse at Corning, just up the street from our home. In those days, crimes of violence were rare in smaller communities, so Corning was buzzing for months with the horror of this one. The prosecution called on my father more than once to testify on medical aspects of the case.

The Smith murder was just the sort of violent subject that my parents would not normally have talked about in my hearing. However, being so involved themselves in this notorious case, they probably could not have avoided commenting on it rather frequently.

I was eight years old then and most impressionable. (I had already been badly frightened when awakened by the wail of the Glass Works siren that greeted the "true" armistice on November 11, 1918.) This time, Jady Kelly, a faceless ogre, kept haunting my dreams.

Only in later life, when I had ceased to be a "fraidy-cat," did I tell my mother how that brutal crime had shaken me up. She was really distressed. "I'm sorry," she said. "Your father and I should have been more careful."

Did the McNamara parents wield the rod or spare it? Let's say the rod was always available. One day Papa chased Tom around the table, brandishing a hairbrush. Tom got away, probably because his father wanted him to. Usually the mere knowledge that the parents were displeased was enough to discourage deviltry.

They caught me red-handed once, and although I escaped a spanking, I still squirm to think of the punishment I did receive.

One day in late summer, I was airily skipping along by the kitchen garden of neighbor Frank Sharp. Noticing there some absolutely colossal radishes, I pulled one up by the roots and took it home. I told my folks, in all innocence, where I had gotten this eye-catching vegetable.

My father reacted in a way I did not expect. He straightway marched me back to Sharp's and knocked on the kitchen door. When Frank came out, I was made to apologize and to return the stolen item. Mr. Sharp was easily mollified and probably amused. He even let me keep the booty. But that radish became my albatross. It was colossal precisely because it had gone to seed, and was too fibrous for human teeth to chew. I have never been fond of radishes since that day. What is more important, I have never stolen another radish – or (so far as I can recall) another anything.

A conscientious father will encourage his young ones to take the initiative, and he will try to create among them a spirit of helpful togetherness. Doc Mac deserved high marks on both counts.

Young Tom, for example, had a real flair for cartooning. His father shared an interest in this hobby, and praised his sketches when they appeared in the high school publication, and even in the daily newspaper. I was hyper-inquisitive at the age of four. Papa therefore bought me the twenty-volume Grolier Book of Knowledge. To this day I have an almost photographic memory of what appeared in that delightful British encyclopedia for children.

My father had a good, if untrained, ear for music. He therefore saw to it that all his kids took instrumental lessons. I was the only one who developed no skill. Adrian became a very good pianist, and young Tom a good violinist. The girls were also more than adequate at the pianoforte.

Indeed, musicians Adrian and Tom even went "semi-pro." By 1898 they and their first cousin, T. Paul McGannon, another violinist, were called upon to perform for visiting friends and even for St. Mary's Aid Society. When they were in high school they were ready to become public entertainers. Adrian, Tom, Paul, and a clarinetist friend, Ralph Dickens, organized a quartet called the "Mac Orchestra." For more than one summer, they were hired to play aboard the "Mary Belle," an excursion boat that plied the blue waters of nearby Keuka Lake. The Doctor enjoyed their music and their gumption.

Music was not the only creative outlet that Adrian and Tom had. One year they and their friends staged a blackface minstrels in a neighborhood barn. A talent scout for the local Alliance Minstrels liked the show, and arranged for its actors to perform in the next edition of his annual "home-talent" production. Around 1920, when I was nine or ten, my own playmates and I presented a vaudeville show in Tevis Holmes's basement. No talent scout would have been impressed by our efforts, but Papa was on hand to applaud us as vigorously as he had applauded my brothers' minstrel show.

I think that Grace McNamara, a daughter of Uncle Will, summed up my father's attitude very well. (Cousin Grace had lived with us in 1919 during her last semester at North Side High School.) "He loved his family very much," she wrote to me in the 1980's, "and he was proud of their accomplishments. I really think he felt he was giving each of you a sense of accomplishment, of your own worth."

The "each of you" is exact. Papa played no favorites. Sometimes he even tested his children's generosity towards each other. Once, for instance, he decided to give Evelyn and Madeline identical diamond rings. But first he took each girl aside and announced that he intended to give a ring to the other. Would the one questioned mind not getting one herself? When Evelyn and Madeline had both replied (however disappointedly) that they would not feel hurt, he was content. Of course, when both received rings, each one was all the more delighted.

Another pleasant picture of the McNamaras' family orientation comes from Grace's sister, Frances McNamara Walling. Uncle Tom, she said, "had a wonderful empathy with children and young people, who adored him. The house was always full of them. Musical evenings with Adrian and Tom and Paul McGannon giving concerts, or just talking to each other." The McNamara parents did encourage them to make their own entertainment in this way; and Mrs. McNamara was always ready to provide corn for popping, taffy for pulling, and lemonade or cocoa for quaffing.

As a late-comer to the family, I had not been able to share in the excitement of the pre-1910 era, but I doted on its "remember-whens."

Like the time Frances rode her sled down a slope specifically forbidden by her father. Her face ended up in an ash pile, noticeably scratched. Now the problem: how could she conceal her disobedience from Papa with her face already branded by the crime? Her solution? She came to supper that night wearing a broad-brimmed hat and full veil!

Or the time when Evelyn went on her first formal date. The youth who invited her arrived at the door in a hired hack. Kid sister, Madeline, and her friend Harriet Bushnell peered through the lace curtains of the parlor to watch the grand departure. As the young prince helped his princess into the carriage, the two little spies' hearts beat faster and faster. It was so incredibly romantic!

Reading some old family letters of late, I have learned that I was becoming a part of the family annals in my "rompers" days. Family notes written to Tom and the girls at school carefully recorded my latest pranks. For one, painting the black Lozier – our first family car – with red paint. Or putting my brother Tom's first professional calling cards into the neighbors' mail boxes. These creative ventures I remember little, if at all. My focus was on the activities of my half-brothers and sisters. Whatever they did was just right!

"Always full of people," said Frances Walling of the Mac home. One reason why we often had callers was that all the Corning parades, patriotic, political and circus, passed by our house, and friends were always welcome to use our folksy front porch as a grandstand.

(Simon and Schuster's nostalgic U.S. picture book, *Hometown U.S.A.* [New York, 1975], shows some of these friends sitting on our porch in June 1904 as a circus parade rumbles by.) But the usual guests at our home were school friends of the children, family friends young and old, and kinsmen from Corning or out-of-town.

The school chums were both Catholic and non-Catholic. Harriet Bushnell, whom I have already mentioned, was a Presbyterian. When her parents (not Corningites) died, this winsome, dimpled, laughing girl was taken in as a ward by her uncle and aunt, a childless couple who lived near us in a dustless house. Uncle James was a tempestuous lawyer, always embroiled, it seemed, in some public controversy. Aunt May, by contrast, was a fastidious woman. She wore pince-nez glasses and a lace stock or a throat ribbon. May was active in the (then) very elitist D.A.R. In fact, she could have functioned admirably as a fourth model for artist Grant Wood's famous painting "Daughters of Revolution."

Having accepted Harriet as a ward, Aunt May sought to make her a snob. For example, she urged her to cultivate the friendship of young "Ellie", whose father was a Corningite of means and influence. But giggly Harriet much preferred the company of giggly Madeline McNamara. "Why ever?" May asked her frostily. "Because Ellie is stuffy, and Madeline is fun!"

Harriet found Doctor and Nell McNamara more understanding than her foster parents. Having gone off to normal school, she met and married another prospective school teacher, Bill Callahan, in 1921. Bill was a quiet, serious young man. No matter; the match was totally unacceptable to Uncle James and Aunt May. Harriet's aunt had often told her that she held three sorts of people in disdain: manual laborers, Irishmen, and Roman Catholics. Harriet's husband had the misfortune to be Irish and Catholic and the son of a bricklayer. So the attorney and his wife seem to have told their niece that for her the latchstring was no longer out.

Doctor Mac eventually learned of Harriet's ostracism. He quickly wrote to tell her that the McNamara home was always open to her and Bill whenever they might choose to visit the hometown.

Among the guests entertained at 32 East First Street were many relatives on both the McNamara and the Dwyer sides of the family. Old Patrick McNamara lived on until 1905. During his later years he often climbed aboard the Erie train at Hornell to ride down for a brief visit with his Corning son. While he was our guest, the little patriarch was usually content to sit in silence chewing "Sweet Burley." Every now and then, however, he would give an abrupt bit of advice to the "young ones." One time when he was visiting, Paul McNamara, Dr. Dan's impish son, was also a guest. At the table, Paul started to mimic his grandpa when the old man wasn't looking. Adrian joined in the mischief. But Papa caught the boys in the act and sent them upstairs. Later he gave them a lecture on respect for elders, punctuating his remarks by a few whacks with a bedroom slipper.

Thomas Alexander perhaps "succeeded" his father as head of the Adrian McNamaras, for he had good judgment and brotherly concern. His brothers and sisters kept in close touch with him, especially when they were having problems. When "Peacock Mary" wedded John L. Shannon and they moved to Corning, she was careful to acquire a house on the same street as the Doctor's. Regal Aunt Fannie McCarthy also came up often from Blossburg to see him. She seems to have had a part in some of his business enterprises.

Dr. Dan used to travel down from Utica about once a year. Dan, always dapper but never quite mature, usually brought along his older children, Paul the mischievous and Sadie – beautiful, jolly, and frilly. Woe to the McNamara ménage if there was a thunderstorm while Uncle Dan was visiting. Many of the Macs were phobic about the electrical storms that rumbled around the Corning valley each summer. Especially if the storms broke at night, there was much running to and fro in the Mac homestead. But Uncle Dan went almost berserk when the lightning began to crackle, and sought refuge underneath the bed.

Dr. Alec of Lockport also paid a yearly visit to his Corning kin. He usually came without his wife, Nell, and daughter, Angela. Alec was calmer than Dan and had a dry wit. He was the most prosperous of the McNamara siblings, not so much through medical income as through shrewd investments. He always gave me the gift of a half-dollar. (I wondered greedily why it was never a whole dollar!) After a couple of pleasant days, he would suddenly disappear, without any farewell. Ungracious? Not at all. He was just a tender-hearted man who disliked family good-byes. His thank-you would arrive later by freight – a bushel of Niagara County peaches.

I have already mentioned Uncle Will. After he moved to Pueblo, Colorado, because of his asthma, he made some notable political and community friendships. One of his friends was the rising young Thomas J. Walsh, future U.S. Senator from Montana. Another was a young journalist named Damon Runyon. In fact, it was William who got Runyon his first news-paper job, on the *Pueblo Chieftain*. But when the deterioration of Will's health finally brought him and his family back east, they ended up in Corning. Dr. Tom kept a watchful eye over his dear disabled brother until he died in 1917. Will's family moved to Washington, D.C. in 1919, but the Corning Macs always remain-ed in close contact with them.

Of course, Doctor Mac could hardly forget the family of Aunt Mary Kennedy, who had been the first to welcome him to Corning. Of her three daughters, only Josephine had children. Jo had married Tom Moran, a prominent local clothier, and raised four daughters whose ages were close to those of the younger Mac children. The fun-loving Morans and the fun-loving Macs saw a good deal of each other.

On the Dwyer side, Kate's sisters Margaret and Helen were very close to the Macs. Maggie Dwyer McGannon and her hus-band John D., a railroader turned dry goods merchant, lived only a block or so away, so their four children and the McNamara chil-dren spent almost as much time in one home as they did in the other.

Mrs. Kate Garrity and her brother, Tom Hayes, were more remote Dwyer cousins. Gentle Kate (whether her husband had died or decamped I never learned) was always ready to help the Doctor's family in times of need. Tom Hayes had moved out to North Platte, Nebraska; but every few years he would return to Corning for a spell. Tom dressed rather shabbily. One time when he came he had replaced a bow of his wire spectacles with a shoestring. I think he lived by peddling. But Tom Hayes was no vagabond. He told his Corning kin marvelous tales about the Great West, and on the slightest invitation declaimed long passages from Shakespeare. In a rather prosaic Irish family, Tom was the Celtic bard.

On the McNamara side, there were no Protestant relatives. There were some on the Dwyer side. When the family of Bridget O'Malley migrated to America (where Bridget was to meet and wed Thomas Dwyer) they scattered. Thomas O'Malley and Mary O'Malley settled in Cuba, New York, a village where there were few Catholics. Both Thomas and Mary married Protestants, and their children were raised Presbyterian. Nevertheless, the Corning McNamaras and Dwyers remained in contact with the Cuba O'Malleys and Renwicks; and although the later descendants drifted apart, the first two generations exchanged visits with regularity.

When deaths occurred, of course, many other kinsmen who came to Corning less frequently were on hand to express their condolences. Around the turn of the century, the Doctor's immediate family was three times visited by death.

The first to die was the Doctor's wife. Lovely Kate ("a saint if there ever was one," said Uncle Alec) passed away on January 23, 1897, at the age of only thirty-three. Her mortal ailment was diagnosed as "strangulation of the bowel." Just a few years later they would call it "appendicitis" and consider it operable.

The Corning newspapers spoke movingly of young Kate as "endowed with a kind and amiable disposition... and possessed of the traits that make woman the loveliest of God's creatures and his greatest handiwork." One of the journalists praised her as a "fine example of true womanhood, devout mother, and most loving wife." Kate left five children, the youngest of whom, six-month-old Madeline, would never remember her. Even Kate's father, Thomas Dwyer, survived his daughter, although by only eleven months.

The blow fell hard upon the widower, who had loved his wife dearly. Fortunately, the extended family was able to come to his rescue. Kate's cousin, Mrs. Garrity, took over the care of little Madeline; and Kate's unmarried sister, Helen, stepped in as the Doctor's housekeeper.

Helen – "Aunt Nell" to her sister's children – was an ideal housekeeper. Humorous, a good manager, an optimist, and much like her sister in outlook, she was very fond of the Mac children, as they were of her. For the next nine years, she carried on admirably well. Substitute motherhood, it turned out, was her true vocation.

In 1906, Doctor Mac decided to ask Nell to marry him. She consented. But before he announced his plans, he first asked the opinion of each of his children. They need not fear, he assured them, about getting a new "Mother." Everything would go on as usual. The kids were pleased to be consulted and gave unanimous approval. Therefore, on May 7, 1906, in St. Mary's Church, Father Bustin joined in marriage Thomas, aged forty-nine, and Nell, aged thirty-eight. Unofficial witnesses were the Doctor's two sons and three daughters. He was truly fortunate in his choice of a second wife. Nell (who always called her husband "Doctor" in public) proved to be another "valiant woman." Indeed, she remained the beloved family matriarch until her death, aged 89, in 1956.

But Doctor Mac had two more great trials. First a son, then a daughter was taken from him. Adrian, his first-born, died on December 8, 1909, aged twenty-three. He had just risen from his night prayers when he was felled by a cerebral hemorrhage. The stroke was both the climax and the explanation of a series of puzzling nervous attacks that he had experienced over the past few years. After a brilliant course in high school, Adrian had gone to the University of Notre Dame. At the end of two years, however, he had a "nervous breakdown." The cause was at first attributed to over-study. He spent some time recuperating and then entered medical school at the University of Buffalo; but a second breakdown occurred after one year. Finally, he had still another collapse after only two months at the law school of Syracuse University.

Adrian had been one of the best-known and most popular

young men in Corning. A local newspaper, in an obituary unusually long for one of his age, said that Adrian represented "the
highest type of young manhood."

The Doctor had only begun to adjust a little to the loss of his
son when his oldest daughter, Frances, followed Adrian to the
grave. Her death was less unexpected. A victim of pernicious
anemia since her graduation from high school in 1907, Frances
had been seriously ill even when her brother died. When death
claimed her on March 14, 1910, she was only twenty.

Corning hearts went out to the respected physician. He had
been called upon, one of the newspapers said, "to undergo a double burden of grief within the last few months." The burden was
indeed almost crushing. Usually so alert and self-controlled, the
Doctor now moved about as if in a trance.

I came into the world on November 3, 1910, nine months after
Frances's death. Only years later did I learn that my birth had
broken my father's spell. A new life in the family gave him new
hope and a new interest. I have always been grateful since then
that I brought such joy to Papa's heart simply by being born!

By 1910, Kate McNamara's three remaining children were
rapidly maturing. Their dad was determined that after high
school they would receive the most appropriate higher education.

Tom Junior had entered the medical school of Syracuse
University as early as 1907. The course in medicine was by then
twice as long as it had been in his father's day. Even after graduating in 1911, he had to do a hospital internship of a year and
more. He interned on Blackwell's Island, New York harbor.
Finally, in 1913, he returned to Corning to enter practice.

When it was understood that young Tom would set up as a
general practitioner in the home town, his father paid $400 to
carpenter Patsy Relihan to replace the side-rear porch at 32 East
First Street with a small office and waiting room. This office
would serve the new doctor for the next eight years. Despite its
modest size, it was well provided with new apparatus, including
X-ray equipment. Papa now proudly mounted a new brass plate
beneath his own on the front of the house. There was still bound

to be some confusion over the two similar names: "Thomas A. McNamara, M.D." and "Thomas L. McNamara, M.D." Corning folks soon found a handy solution. They simply referred to the father as "Old Doc Mac" and the son as "Young Doc Mac." And the nicknames stuck.

"Old Doc" naturally helped "Young Doc" in the slow process of acquiring a clientele. He passed over to him some of his own patients. Now, not all of the long-time patients wanted to be transferred, even from father to son. For instance, when Papa sent Tom to call on Mrs. Mary Cavalier, Mary told the young medic to go fly a kite. Tom reported this put-down to his dad. Old Doc sent him right back to Mary. That was an end to it, and she offered no further objections. As a matter of fact, the Cavaliers became as attached to the junior doctor as they had been to the senior.

In World War I, when Tom got a commission in the Army medical corps, Dad took over his still small practice for the duration. As a physician in several stateside army hospitals, young Doc picked up much medical and orthopedic information that he would later share with his father. After the Armistice, however, time hung heavy on Tom's hands while his father back home was struggling more and more with the increasing demands of both practices. Old Doc therefore decided to pull some political wires to get his son released. Alanson B. Houghton, Corning's leading industrialist, had just been elected to Congress on the Republican slate. The Doctor sought his aid in securing Tom's discharge. Congressman Houghton obliged. Although it took a while to untangle the Army red tape, Lieutenant McNamara was "honorably released from active duty" on August 9, 1919. A short while later he was again receiving patients in his tiny Corning office.

McNamara and Son had made a good professional team from the start, always available to each other as consultants, co-surgeons, or co-obstetricians. The confinement case of Florence Markert Rose is a good illustration of their team in action.

Edward Rose and his wife, Florence Markert, very much wanted a family, but a miscarriage and its consequences lessened their hopes. However, Florence did conceive again in 1924. When the time of expectancy drew near, Old Doc, knowing that the delivery would be complicated, brought his son into the case.

Mrs. Rose's travail extended over two days. In its later stages the physicians kept constant vigil at the bedside. They were deeply concerned: not only was the mother close to exhaustion; the heart of the unborn child was beating irregularly.

Suddenly, on December 11, 1924, tiny Evelyn emerged with rending violence. She was limp and ominously silent. Her mother was bleeding profusely.

Old Doc said to Tom, "See if the baby is alive. Do what you can." Then he turned back to Florence to stem the bleeding and deal with the lacerations.

The son first administered emergency baptism. Then he attempted mouth-to-mouth resuscitation – a rather new technique in those days. Finally, after what must have seemed to be an age, baby Evelyn took a shuddering breath and then just yelled – loud and strong. Tom grinned at his father, wrapped the infant in a blanket, and laid her down in a safe place. Old Doc nodded approvingly. "I thought she was gone. Congratulations, Doctor Mac!" Then the pair set at work applying "Murphy buttons" to the mother's jagged lesions as temporary "sutures." Florence recovered only slowly, but she and Edward remained ever grateful to the Mac medics for the only family they would ever have.

After the death of his father, young Tom continued for years as a distinguished general practitioner. In fact, he was still serving a few loyal patients at the age of 93 when he suffered the fall that indirectly led to his death on July 15, 1981.

Once Tom's higher education had been launched, Evelyn got her turn. In 1911, her father sent her to St. Elizabeth's, a Catholic women's college at Morristown, New Jersey. During her three semesters there, Evelyn made many lovely friends, whom she soon invited to Corning to spend their vacations. After leaving St. Elizabeth's by her own choice, she spent a few years at home, studying music and dancing and preparing her hope chest. A gifted dancer, she followed the example of the then popular Irene and Vernon Castle, and supported herself for a while by teaching ballroom and folk-dancing. Then in 1918 she went to Washington, where she secured a wartime office job.

"I hope she meets some statesman in Washington," Mom wrote to Madeline, half-joking, half-serious. For what Evelyn the affectionate, Evelyn the practical, most wanted was neither a degree nor a career, but a husband and family. No "statesman" courted her in the capital, but when she went to New York to work a year or so later, she met her dream. Harry F. Van Wagner, a handsome native of Manhattan, was the son of a New Amsterdam Dutch father and an Irish-born mother. They lived in the High Bridge section of the Bronx. Harry, a World War I veteran, was on the sales force of Atlas Portland Cement.

When Evelyn and Harry were married in Corning on Columbus Day, 1921, the bride's father gave her a first-class wedding (canopies at both church and home!). A year later Evelyn returned to Corning in time for Papa to deliver Katherine, his first granddaughter. He also delivered Mary, the second of her three surviving daughters in 1925. Evelyn brought her children back to Corning a couple of times a year. For her, the old family residence was home par excellence. Unfortunately, Evelyn Van Wagner survived her father by only four years, dying in 1931 at the age of thirty-eight.

Madeline, in turn, went to St. Elizabeth's College in 1915. However, in view of her special interest in public speaking and dramatics, she transferred in 1916 to Emerson College of Oratory in Boston. There she earned a baccalaureate of literary interpretation in 1919.

Madeline's aims were less focused than Evelyn's. At one point she had an offer to join the acting company of Broadway producer John Golden. Her father disapproved. The world of the professional theater, he thought, involved just too many risks. For several years, therefore, Madeline coached high school speech and drama at Glen Cove, Long Island. Later, she worked in Manhattan as a salesperson and a hostess at Schrafft's restaurants; as a drama teacher and summer theater coach and performer in Washington and the Adirondacks; and as a monologuist, presenting one-woman dramas to school and club audiences. During World War II, the Red Cross employed her as a recreational director in southern military hospitals. Returning to Corning after the War, she sold antiques and supported herself in a series of positions involving public relations, particularly at the new Corning Glass Center.

Although the most "socialite" of the Doctor's family, winning a host of friends through her helpful interest, Madeline never married. Proposals there were, but she eventually rejected them. The main reason, I believe, is that she could find no man who measured up to her adored father. To the day she died in 1974, she reflected much of his idealism, but little of his realism.

We must turn back again, however, to the years right after World War I, when all the family were still at home. Realizing that his brood would soon scatter, Old Doc thought it would be nice to take a vacation or two together.

Because he was tied down professionally while in Corning, the Doctor and his family had thus far done their traveling in groups rather than as a unit. (True, they all went together by rail to the "Old Home Reunion" held at Adrian, New York. But that was a one-day affair – July 24, 1913.) Furthermore, they had never taken any major auto trips together.

By 1919, Papa had bought a (new?) seven-passenger Studebaker touring car, so he decided that we would all go to New England. The following summer we went to Canada. He kept a travel-log both years, and on our return wrote a journal of each expedition.

The adventure of 1919 ran from August 16 to August 22. It took us to Peterborough, New Hampshire, where Madeline was a counselor at Sargent Summer Camp for girls.

Motoring was still problematic in those days. Thus, in 1919, we had not gone any farther than Binghamton, New York, when a tire blew out. A new tire, at that. Farther along, we ran into a drenching rain. It took all the "starch" out of Papa's Panama hat before we could snap on the isinglass side curtains fore and aft.

But at least the Doctor could write of the stretch of road between Oneonta and Albany, New York, that we "sailed over good roads at about twenty miles an hour."

For my father, the most memorable episode of the New England trip was his visit to the tomb of Jim Fisk in the cemetery at Brattleboro, Vermont. Fisk, remember, was the Erie Railroad tycoon the news of whose assassination had so startled my dad in 1872 when he heard it on the telegraph at Adrian, New York. Now, as a veteran physician, he contemplated the imposing but dilapidated cemetery monument of James Fisk. At once there came to his mind the poet Gray's melancholy line, "The paths of glory lead but to the grave."

Trip number two ran from August 23 to August 31, 1920. We went to Clayton, New York (and, of course, took a motorboat tour of the Thousand Islands). Then we drove to Montreal. At Montreal we took an overnight steamer to Quebec. From Quebec we went by trolley to the shrine of St. Anne de Beaupré, to whom my father had a strong devotion. That was our terminus; the rest was a return trip.

Today, journeys of this sort are routine, and have few inconveniences. Eighty years ago, especially to a family unused to long excursions into "strange" states and "foreign" countries, our two trips were as exciting as Magellan's pioneering trip around the globe.

But, it was always nice to get home again. Papa concluded his Canadian journal with a pat on the hood for the Studebaker. There had been, he wrote, "not so much as the history of a dirty plug in the machine."

When my father died, the editor of the Corning *Leader* wrote of him, "Dr. McNamara being a home-loving man, his home life was ideal."

Now, no family has an "ideal" life in the strict sense. Memory has a way, however, of erasing many of the less pleasant recollections. The more I forget the little trials and reflect on the major joys, the more I agree with that editor.

Doctor Mac's home was indeed a warm nest!

— CHAPTER SIX —

"To Heal, To Comfort, To Console"

In 1916 somebody gave Madeline a scrapbook. One section was reserved for the signatures and "remarks" of friends. Papa was, of course, asked to sign.

"Thos. A. McNamara," he wrote with a flourish and unusual legibility: "Corning, N.Y., December 16-16." In the column labeled "remarks," he added: "The only comments, dear Madeline, I can make herein are, this is my 60th birthday, your first return from Boston for Xmas, and to thank God for the many gifts bestowed on me, among which you are one."

The Doctor had a special tenderness for this motherless daughter for whom he had had to serve as both parents in one. His entry in the scrapbook also marked the beginning of the last decade of his life.

In the early 1920's, the old home gradually emptied itself. If Evelyn brought the children back each Christmas and summer, her permanent address was now in the Bronx, or later, in New Jersey. Tom moved his office into the Liberty Theater building in 1921, married in 1924, and eventually adopted two boys. Madeline was working in the New York City area. Thus I was the only McNamara child still at home: a pre-teen, rather worried about having soon to depart from the pleasant securities of St. Mary's School and to enter the vast "ecumenical" world of Corning Free Academy. Having my druthers, too, about the whole prospect of becoming an adult!

Whether or not our house was more quiet than before, the Doctor went about his professional business as usual. When Republican Samuel E. Quackenbush was elected mayor in 1922, he appointed Dad city physician.

The national recession of 1921-1922 brought extensive unemployment to Corning. The New York Central Shops laid off many hands. The Corning Glass Works also dismissed a large number of employees, and reduced the wages of those it retained. Since $10,000 of the sum pledged that year to the Corning Charity Chest went unpaid, the town's unemployed were in double jeopardy. Fortunately, business began to look up again by mid-1922, and the Glass Works, the city's main industry, embarked upon an encouraging program of expansion. From then on, the nation not only recovered but entered a hectic prosperity that would last until the market crash of 1929.

Doctor Mac would not have to live through the crash and the Great Depression that followed. He was thus able to view with proud optimism the many signs of local progress that surfaced in the 1920's. The opening of a country club in 1920-1921 was, for instance, a stylish event. Although "Old Doc" would have had small interest in its athletic and social aspects, "Young Doc" took out a membership in which his brother and sisters could share. The former Mayor was especially happy to see the dedication, in 1923, of a new cement vehicular bridge across the Chemung River at Pine Street. This was the bridge he had proposed as mayor a dozen years before. Denison Park continued to serve its purpose well. Doc attended the dedication of its ornamental main gateway in 1921 and was pleased when the park acquired a public swimming pool in 1923. One year later, a welcome new wing of Corning Hospital was opened.

Some local events of the twenties were, of course, less happy. At mid-decade, for instance, the Ku Klux Klan raised a furtive head at Corning. Fiery crosses appeared with some regularity on the heights of Rose Hill. Whether these were "official" or not, the very sight of them was disconcerting to Corning Blacks, Jews, and Catholics. Fortunately, the Klan never won many followers in Corning proper, although it apparently attracted more members in the countryside.

Doctor Mac also continued during his sixties to write essays and (if possible) deliver them as lectures. A religious quality still permeated these compositions – sometimes overtly, sometimes with more nuance. Thus, one of his manuscripts was a frank apologia for the Catholic Church. In it he wrote that he himself was a Catholic not just because his parents had been Catholic, but because religion is an essential trait of man and demands to be carefully cultivated. He quoted approvingly the aphorism, "The history of the world is the history of its religion, and the history of religion is the history of the world." To emphasize his contention that Catholicism had made a unique contribution to history, he cited words of praise for the Church by two Protestant ministers and by the British Protestant historian, Thomas B. Macaulay. It is highly likely that Doc delivered this Catholic *fervorino* to the local council of the Knights of Columbus.

More shaded was the Christian ingredient in his talks to mixed religious audiences. There he usually wrote on science as a scientist who was also a believer. In one essay he was critical of the evolutionists' quest for the "missing link." He pointed out that the skull and skeletal remains of *homo sapiens* had remained basically the same throughout the ages. In another study, he dealt with astronomy. While he admitted that celestial bodies exert some influence on human behavior, he disallowed any substantial control by them over the human will.

The articles on evolution and the celestial bodies were probably delivered to the Corning Medical Association. So also, perhaps, was another lecture called "Dreams," which was printed in the Corning *Evening Leader*. Here was a meditation on the human conscious and subconscious. We can, he said, analyze the human body scientifically till kingdom come; but to the end "we are baffled when we try to analyze the *process of thinking* or to get a peep into the worlds of mystery that are behind the evolution of a single thought." One day scientific experiments might indeed be able to bring living matter out of inorganic material. This would be a wholesome development if it led to a better understanding of life itself. Nevertheless, he insisted, "the greater our efforts in such attempts, the more profoundly must we be convinced of a supreme Intelligence that creates, governs and controls the universe in its own wise, inscrutable and mysterious ways."

Although the Doctor was neither a trained scholar nor a professional writer, he could, at his best, hold the attention of a "middle brow" audience. The editor of the *Leader* would later say that Doctor Mac delivered speeches "which were models of grace, diction, sense and humor. His nature was philosophic, his attitude reverent and his poise in public utterance one of unfailing good humor and delicacy."

The article "Whither Are We Drifting?" – a typescript of 21 pages of blue hunt-and-peck – was less optimistic than his other manuscripts. Written around 1924, it listed several current trends that he considered ominous. One was the Oregon state law of 1922 (fortunately declared unconstitutional in 1925 by the U.S. Supreme Court) that would have outlawed all non-public schools. Others were: a drift towards the centralization of power; civil discord; military menace; the federalization of education; graft in the courts; disregard for the federal constitution; ambition for political domination; religious intolerance (especially the Ku Klux Klan); socialism; bolshevism; race suicide; expanding divorce. Some of these worries depressed him as a Catholic; most of them were the concerns of any idealistic and religious American of the day. As was his custom, he quoted comments by a variety of contemporary writers on these disturbing matters. Whether he ever found an audience for "Whither Are We Drifting?" I cannot say.

Gradually I began to become better acquainted with my father as the 1920's went on; and he, I think, began to be a little better acquainted with the son of his latter years. One of the earliest and most pleasant recollections I have of feeling closer to him was that night in April 1920 when he took the family to the movies.

It was a decision made late in the day. Papa told us only that afternoon that the treat would be on him. The offer was surprising enough. The rest of the family were regular movie-goers, but he seldom had time or inclination to attend. I remember chortling for joy at the prospect. So at 7 P.M., we all walked around the corner to the Opera House where he purchased audience seats for Cecil B. DeMille's *Male and Female*.

Despite its suggestive title, *Male and Female* was family fare: it was none other than J. M. Barrie's delightful comedy, *The Admirable Crichton*. Thomas Meighan played Crichton, the butler who became king of the snooty family that he had served, when that family was wrecked on a desert island. Theodore Roberts was typecast as the irascible father of the shipwrecked ménage. A young Gloria Swanson was his snobbish daughter. I thoroughly enjoyed the show, chuckling along with my father; and to this day I can hum the theme tunes that the pianist played to accompany this silent film. When the two delightful hours were over, we all walked over to Terbell-Calkins Drugstore and climaxed the evening with a round of ice creams.

Four years later, at the age of thirteen, I was already becoming interested in literature, and heeding my teachers' insistence on good spelling and grammar. Papa was then typing out an essay – I think it was "Whither Are We Drifting?" He asked me to read the script and tell him what I thought. Flattered by this show of confidence, I read what he gave me, understanding it more or less, and discovering a few mistakes in grammar and spelling.

When I reported my reaction, he looked me in the eye, brightly and fondly. Evidently he was saying to himself, "The boy is showing a critical sense. I like that!" He thanked me for my suggestions, adopted them, and let me read other portions of the text.

Many years afterward, my mother told me that he had advised her more than once, "Nell, never deny books to Bob!" I only regret that I did not get to know my father better thereafter, on a man-to-young-man basis. Unfortunately, in the fall of 1926, when I was only fifteen-going-on-sixteen, he contracted an infection of the prostate gland. The best known treatments were used to counter it, but these were the days before the wonder drugs, and, all efforts failing, the ailment became chronic.

John Heyniger lived across the street from us. One very chilly day about this time, John, happening to look out the window, saw my father pacing our front porch without a coat, and (more oddly) without a hat. "Ella," John said to his wife, "look at old Doctor Mac walking on his porch without his coat and hat. He's remarkable. All the zest of a youngster!" Actually Papa was out in the chill air not because he was hardy but because he was burning up with fever.

In October 1926, he and Young Doc decided he had better go for surgery. The place chosen was the Robert Packer Hospital at Sayre, Pennsylvania, a fine institution some forty miles east of Corning. I stayed home, of course. The house seemed eerily empty, with this ever-present-ever-absent man nowhere about. It was odd to see his long-suffering Dodge coupé standing idle in the barn.

The operation was performed in November. Papa was sufficiently restored, I recall, to be home for Christmas. Soon his handwriting began to reappear in the account books, replacing that of my mother and brother. But his "vacation" was not long. He returned to Sayre and had a second operation on February 10, 1927. This time he did not rally. On February 17, all the family, including myself, were called to his bedside.

For the first time in my sixteen years, I saw death relentlessly at work. Was this really my father lying there – his cheeks sunken and unshaven, his eyes glazed, his breathing short and labored? Was this the man who loved the smell of moss roses, enveloped in a miasma of pus? Mercifully, I was sent from the bedroom after a few minutes. At least, I do not recall being on hand at 11:30 P.M. when the rattle stilled in his throat and Thomas Alexander McNamara was gathered to his Irish forefathers. His age was then seventy years, two months and one day.

It was now too late to go elsewhere, so my mother told me to curl up in one of the wicker chairs on the sun porch. Never before had I slept in a chair, never had I experienced such restless discomfort. But the encounter with death itself was, I think, the chief reason why the night of February 17-18, 1927 turned out to be the longest and most desolate of my life. My memory of the wake in our front parlor is laced with the odor of Easter lilies. It took a while to get used to the black dresses and hat that my mother would wear for the next twelvemonth. The burial was wintry.

True to his parental responsibility, Papa had left us all well provided for. If a few of his stock bequests were of little or no value, he was still able to bequeath close to $100,000. Religion and kindred were both remembered. A special legacy went to Eleanor, the widow of his brother, Will McNamara. Carefully arranging for his own widow, he gave special instructions that she use whatever was necessary to give me an education equivalent to that which the rest of his children had enjoyed.

When I read what other Corningites said about my deceased father, I began to appreciate his stature more than ever before. The *Evening Leader*, for instance, asked the local physicians what they thought of their late colleague. (They had attended his funeral Mass in a body.)

"His sterling worth as a physician," one of them testified, "has placed him in the highest class of modern workers in our profession." Another termed him "a man whom I admire greatly as a man and as a physician." Said still another colleague, "He was the personification of honor and trustworthiness." The president of Corning Hospital spoke of the Doctor as "courteous, considerate and high-principled." Corning's postmaster remembered him as a mayor of "ability and integrity."

W. Allen Underhill of the *Evening Leader* analyzed Dr. McNamara most discerningly. He praised him as a person of many achievements. An honest and inspiring civil servant, leader and patriot. A personage popular because of his charism as well as his professional skill. A man of unsparing energy. A convinced Christian. A sympathetic figure, a calming presence, one who could bring out the best in his fellow-man. "Dr. McNamara," he concluded, "leaves this world having made it richer and better and himself well beloved as one of our greatest citizens."

One hesitates to accept at face value eulogies that appear in a small town newspaper. However, what tended to confirm their sentiments, if not necessarily their superlatives, was the host of unsolicited testimonies from Dr. McNamara's patients. He had entered the folklore of their family history, and years later the children and grandchildren of those patients would still recount what Doc Mac had done for their elders.

Here is a little story that illustrates what one might call the "Doctor Mac Legend:"

Nine years after my father's death I was ordained a Catholic priest. Although I was assigned to teach in Rochester, New York, I was always able to make the 100-mile trip to Corning in time for Christmas. Between 1940 and 1953, the pastor cajoled me annually into saying a "few words" at the midnight Mass.

One Christmas Eve, two middle-aged men of St. Mary's parish came to church after having begun their Christmas celebration a little too early. They sat in the pew in front of my nieces Mary and Betty and began to talk loudly about irrelevant matters, continuing their gab even after Mass started. Then came the singing of the Gospel, after which I put in my appearance in the pulpit. The steadier of the two chatterers now nudged the other with his elbow and pointed up to the preacher. "You'd better be quiet now," he said. "That's old Doc Mac's son!"

Had my father been able to face his eulogists, he would quite likely have said that throughout his professional life he had only tried to live up to the Hippocratic Oath that he had taken at graduation in 1882. In the old form of this oath, the medical doctor promised to teach others the art of healing; to do only what was "for the benefit of my patients, and to abstain from whatever is deleterious and mischievous"; to respect both the confidence and the personal dignity of those whom he treated; and to live and practice "with purity and holiness." "May it be granted to me," the neophyte doctor then prayed, "to enjoy life and the practice of the art, respected by all men, in all times. But should I trespass and violate this oath may the reverse be my lot."

The sentiments of the old pagan formula were noble. People like Dr. McNamara further ennobled it by interpreting it in a

Christian manner. Meanwhile, the physician, and most of all the general practitioner, who had to be "all things to all men," was painfully aware of his own fallibility. There was always the danger of making an inadvertently incorrect diagnosis. There was always the barrier of human limitation. When the doctor had done all that he could, professionally, without effecting a cure, he had simply to leave the rest in God's hands. Centuries ago an anonymous French physician had framed an axiom that humbly summarized what the medical man can achieve and what he cannot. "Guérir parfois, soulager souvent, consoler toujours": "Cure sometimes, relieve often, console always."

Every old-time G.P. could have used that phrase as both his watchword and his epitaph. There is no better illustration of how Thomas A. McNamara made it his principle than the death of DeLacy Cash.

Charlie Cash, DeLacy's son, was in his late seventies when he stopped me one day on a Corning street to tell me the story. The Cashes were a Protestant family of no great prosperity. Years before, they had chosen my father for their physician because they respected him as a scientist and as a man. In the early 1920's, DeLacy was well on in years and increasingly bedridden. The Doctor could see that the sands of his life were running out.

One day the family went into DeLacy's room and found him sitting. Somehow he had swung his legs out of the bed and now he remained there speechless, staring into space. The Cashes sent at once for the Doctor.

When my father arrived, Charlie told me, he just sat down and looked at DeLacy for several minutes without saying anything.

Finally Charlie asked him, "What should we do, Doctor? Should we make him lie down?" "No," Papa finally answered. "Just sit beside him and put your arm around him." Charlie did. The old man died a few minutes later.

There were tears in Cash's eyes as he told me this story of an event that had happened thirty years before. He shook his head in wonder. "I only hope that when my time comes, I can die as peacefully! "

Index

About the Author

Father Robert F. McNamara is the youngest son of Dr. Thomas A. McNamara (1856–1927) and the only child of his second wife Helen (Nell) Dwyer. He was born in November 3, 1910 in Corning, New York. Corning, although noted as a glass-making center, is a small city in very rural and remote Steuben County.

A graduate of Georgetown and Harvard Universities and of the Gregorian Theological University in Rome, Italy, he was ordained a Rochester diocesan priest in 1936. For 43 years he taught church history at St. Bernard's seminary, Rochester, retiring in 1981 – the same year that St. Bernard's itself closed its doors after 88 years of distinguished educational service. Professor McNamara's major writings have been on Catholic institutional history. His first book (1948), *A Century of Grace*, was the carefully researched story of his home parish, St. Mary's, in Corning. The internationally hailed *The American College in Rome* followed (1956), a definitive centennial account of his Roman Alma Mater, the Pontifical North American College. In 1958 Bishop James E. Kearney asked him to prepare *The Diocese of Rochester*, another scholarly commemorative, published in 1968 (and in an updated second edition, 1998).

Father McNamara is also the archivist of the Diocese of Rochester (1976 to present). But his activities and writings have focused as well on the secular history of the Corning and Rochester areas.

Although a "professor emeritus" for over two decades, Father McNamara has continued to write. For more than 20 years he has contributed a weekly saint's life to the bulletin of the St. Thomas the Apostle Church, in Rochester, where he was in residence, 1981 to 2002. Now living in a retirement community, he continues to supply these weekly biographies, which have attracted considerable attention on the Internet. (http://www.stthomasirondequoit.com/SaintsAlive/)

Broadly educated, therefore, in general and particularly in history, and skilled in historical narrative, Father McNamara was well equipped to write this tender, wise memoir of his medical father. It is the simple tale of the son of an Irish immigrant who, in a still "primitive" era of medical science chose to devote his life to the care of his diversified upstate neighbors, and by his talent, integrity and compassion won the tribute of their deep respect.